DREAMLAND

By Graham McColl and available from Headline

'78: How a Nation Lost the World Cup

DREAMLAND

GRAHAM McCOLL

hachette
SCOTLAND

First published in 2010 by HACHETTE SCOTLAND
An imprint of HACHETTE UK

1

Cataloguing in Publication Data is available from the British Library

Trade paperback ISBN 978 0 7553 1937 4

Typeset in Palatino by Ellipsis Books Limited, Glasgow

Printed and bound in Great Britain by
Clays Ltd, St Ives plc

Headline's policy is to use papers that are natural, renewable
and recyclable products and made from wood grown in sustainable forests.
The logging and manufacturing processes are expected to conform to
the environmental regulations of the country of origin.

HACHETTE SCOTLAND
An Hachette UK Company
338 Euston Road
London NW1 3BH

www.hachettescotland.co.uk
www.hachette.co.uk

For Jackie – and the
first ten years of marriage in our
own dreamland

ACKNOWLEDGEMENTS

Special thanks to Bob McDevitt, Wendy McCance, Rhea Halford, Stan and to Lawrie Reilly, Scotland great.

KEEPING THE PLACE

'I wish I'd never billy-well heard of this World Cup, Janet!' George Graham splutters from behind his desk as the Scottish Football Association's tea-lady manoeuvres her way into his office, nudging open with her left shoulder its heavy oaken door with practised ease at the same time as nimbly balancing a tray laden with teapot, cups, saucers, newly toasted muffins, various chocolate biscuits and cakes. 'It's caused more of a song and dance than Gracie Fields ever did,' Graham brays, 'and it has given a lot of people a lot of ideas above their station! And I wish whomever it was that discovered South America had never bothered their backside! What did the Brazilians or the Argentinians or the Peruvians do in the war? Hee-haw! Now, while we're struggling to get together the basics of life again after saving the world from that madman Hitler, these FIFA people are interfering and trying to bring to an end the game that we gave to the globe! It's beyond hilarity, it really is . . .

'They're also saying that Hitler and his henchmen are actually hiding out in South America. Can you believe it? Maybe he's behind all this, this World Cup. As well as all that, there wouldn't even be a FIFA if it weren't for us. You'll remember, Janet, that match we held just after the war at Hampden Park – Great Britain against the Rest of the World – well that was a fundraising stunt for FIFA and if it hadn't been for that game they'd have gone broke, bankrupt, kaput. Then this is how they reward us.'

Janet Haugh puts the tray down carefully on the edge of the SFA secretary's desk. 'Yes, Mr Graham,' she says, respectfully, turning over the two cups onto their saucers and pouring. 'That's fresh blackberry jam to go with the muffins, Mr Graham. I managed to get an extra ration of sugar so I made it this morning. Shall I tell Mr Kirkwood to come through now?'

'Yes, yes, Janet, yes, please do,' Graham says, calmer now for his letting loose his feelings, 'and that's very nice about the jam. Thank you.'

'Oh, Mr Graham, the sweet salesman, Mr O'Flanagan, dropped by at lunchtime and popped in half a dozen Fry's Cream bars for you. He said they're "on the house".'

'O'Flanagan, eh? Can't say I care much for that fellow but if he's dispensing favours such as that, we can't turn him down, now can we? How he's getting his hands on Fry's chocolate bars in these times I don't know. I suppose he'll be looking for tickets for the match next week. Still, what are a couple of tickets when he's dishing out such rare luxuries?

I'll collect them on my way out this evening. Thank you, Janet.'

Droplets of rain splatter against the first-floor window of the SFA's offices at Carlton Place as Graham sits back in his chair and contemplates the River Clyde, grey and churning along slowly beneath a spring sky that is its mirror image. The man known in the press as a stormy petrel is in subdued mood this deadening April afternoon. He rises and, using a pair of tongs beside the grate, places enough precious lumps of coal on the fire to see it through the remainder of the chilly day. After more than two decades as SFA secretary and having presided over a stable, settled time for the sport, even through the war hiatus, now he feels assaulted by the forces of modernity and, especially, by the twin threats from Brazil and Colombia that have put him under pressure like never before.

It has all come to a head two days previously. A goal from Roy Bentley, the England forward, sent Scotland tumbling to a home defeat in the annual match against the Auld Enemy. During normal times, the Scottish supporters would have been content to swear revenge on the English at Wembley in a year's time but these are abnormal times and much rage is, instead, being turned towards the SFA. FIFA has generously decreed, in honour of Britain's status in founding the game, that the top two in the Home International Championship will be allowed entry to the World Cup finals, to be held in Brazil in summer 1950. England's win has seen them top the table; the Scots have finished second. Graham, though, has long stated firmly that he would only take a Scottish squad to Brazil if they were champions of Britain. Even some English players have pleaded for leniency on their opponents' behalf – making direct appeals to individuals inside the SFA in the immediate aftermath of Saturday's match – but Graham is uninterested and will not be swayed.

Additionally, trouble is brewing from the direction of Colombia, where the leading clubs are offering top British players more money in a year than they could earn in a career at home. Scots are prominent among those in demand. British league football remains preeminent in the world, with Scots widely regarded as its principal entertainers and conjurors of magic and they are thus attractive to the Colombians as they seek an injection of foreign talent into their football. In his desk drawer, Graham has a secret list of no fewer than 180 Scottish players who have asked Joe Dodds, a Scottish agent for the Colombians, to arrange a deal for them.

'Oh, there you are, Kirkwood,' Graham calls out cheerily as the SFA treasurer enters the room. Robert Kirkwood, a tall, rangy man, with a slim moustache, dark brown wavy hair and a cigarette constantly on the go, never fails to lift Graham's spirits. Kirkwood exercises his duties with a light touch that contrasts with that of the dogged, stolid SFA secretary and his very presence in the room buoys Graham, not a smiling animal, lifting his confidence that he can see these tough times through.

'There's talk today in the town that HM Government may be about to go a bit easier on the old sugar rationing,' Kirkwood says as he takes a seat on the other side of Graham's desk and draws a cut-glass ashtray towards him. 'That should cheer folks up a bit after that sorry spectacle against England on Saturday.'

'Yes, yes; anything will do at this time,' Graham responds as Kirkwood plucks a chocolate éclair from the tray, delicately puts it to his lips and manages to consume it cleanly, without endangering the spotlessness of his neatly cut, blue,

three-piece woollen suit. The treasurer gazes absent-mind-
edly out of the window at the unremarkable sky, before taking
up his cup of tea and languidly rekindling his conversation
with Graham.

'You know how I feel about it all, George, don't you?'

'Yes I do,' Graham answers. 'I am aware that you think it
a good idea that we go to this World Cup but I agreed with
the Irish and the Welsh that we would only accept a World
Cup place if we won the group and I cannot go back on my
word now!' Graham, agitated, brings his fist down on the
table, making his cup jump, displacing some of its contents
and sending a couple of Tunnocks caramel logs tumbling to
the floor. 'Sorry, Robert, it's just that all this is getting to me.
I feel as though we're being publicly blackmailed to go to this
World Cup and I won't stand for it.'

Kirkwood nods reassuringly then continues. 'You know,
George, old chap, it's all very well for the Irish and Welsh to
agree to such a thing but you know, and I know, and they
know just how slim their chances were of finishing first or
second. We beat the Irish 8–2 over in Belfast, remember, and
the Welsh didn't offer much resistance when we beat them
here at Hampden. It suited them to hold us to that agreement
– no skin off their noses and it helps their feeling of security.
England never were party to such an agreement, were they?
And you can be jolly well sure that if they had finished second
to us they would still be winging it on that aeroplane down
to jolly old Rio next month. I say, chocks away and we join
them. I must also say that there is as much at stake for those
of us inside this building as for anyone else.'

'What do you mean?'

'Well,' Kirkwood continues, after drawing slowly on his
cigarette and carefully tipping the ash, 'I spoke to Stanley

5

Rous when our English chums came to the boardroom after Saturday's game and the word is that my place on the FIFA international board is in severe jeopardy if we don't go to Brazil. Stanley also told me, on the q-t, that, as secretary of the Football Association, he feels he is next best thing to a shoo-in to be the next FIFA president when Ivo Schricker retires after the World Cup, and that Arthur Drewry, the England selector, could be getting the chairman's job. So our English friends, in turn, will be handing out favours, including some jolly good jobs, in the next year or two – and that's where you come in, if you get my drift . . .

'Bear in mind, old bean, that this whole FIFA thing is going to explode over the next few years with the World Cup and what not – Stanley is sure of it. It's going to be quite a beano and the top bananas are going to have a jolly good ride on the back of it all.

'Besides all that, I honestly feel that this World Cup thingy is a pretty splendid idea. Flavio Costa, the Brazil manager, was another of our guests on Saturday and he assured me that the whole thing is going to go with a bang: he says the stadium they're building in Rio to hold it this year is going to be the biggest in the world – huge enough to hold 200,000. Doesn't that speak for itself? He entreated me to do everything in my power to try to get you to change your mind because the Brazilians would love to have us over there. Do you know that he'd come all the way over from South America and he'd stayed at the Marine Hotel down in Troon for several days just to plead with you? You refused even to meet him. I must say I was very disappointed in that, old boy.

'Anyway, what's the time? Quarter past four already. Time I wasn't here. I'll leave you to chew it over . . .

'And remember, you'd be a hero to the chap in the street

if you were to come around. I was in the Horse Shoe bar – dropped in for a glass of porter after lunch at the Central Hotel – and the fellows in the booth next to me were working themselves into a frightful froth over the team not going to the World Cup tourney. I won't repeat every word they said – I shall spare you that – but, in a nutshell, they weren't too impressed by your sticking to your position. So you can only do yourself and everyone else a lot of good by performing an about-turn.

'Well, I've got an appointment with the chairman of St Johnstone for a spot of golf up at Gleneagles tomorrow so, see you Weds old boy – toodle-pip!'

As Kirkwood glides out of Graham's office he takes a quick, assessing glance over his shoulder at the SFA secretary, sitting deep in thought, his rotund trunk and chubby face, plus thick, round spectacles, making him look more than ever like the Michelin Man, observes Kirkwood; that, or an outsized baby. 'Hope that's done the trick,' Kirkwood mumbles underneath his breath, flashing a ready smile at Janet Haugh as he collects hat, coat and brolly from the stand in the lobby and prepares to meet head-first the bracing elements.

Graham, meanwhile, levers himself up from behind his desk and, hands behind back, face tight with irritation, begins pacing up and down the length of his office. While Kirkwood's presence always cheers him, there is, also, almost always some dissatisfaction, a feeling of inadequacy, on Graham's part when the man leaves. This time is no different. Graham had sought reassurance from his colleague but has instead been left with a whole lot of loose ends and nagging doubts, which is just what he did not want. 'That's just what I did not want,' he bellows to the empty room, 'that's just what I did not want!'

A brown leather, lace-up football, a gift from Tomlinson's,

the sports equipment distributors, is lying in the corner of the room and in his fury and frustration, Graham rolls it out and gives it a powerful dunt with his right foot. He intends a rebound off the office wall but loses balance slightly as he strikes the ball and it flies off his smartly polished brogue at a sharp angle and goes straight through the window. Janet Haugh comes running in, as do two junior administrators, to find a puce-faced Graham being cooled by the chilly blast of fresh air now entering his lair through the newly cracked window.

'Blasted kids!' Graham yells, affecting to look down into the street for the alleged miscreants. 'What do they think they're doing, playing football in the street? Look, that's their ball there, must have run away without it. Some of those scallywags from the Gorbals, no doubt. There ought to be a law against it; shouldn't be allowed . . . why they want to kick a ball around in the street I don't know.

'Eh, Hogg, could you ask the glazier to come out right away and get that window fixed?'

· 1950 · 1950 · 1950 · 1950 · 1950 · 1950 · 1950 · 1950 · 1950 · 1950 ·

If there is one element in George Graham's character in which he takes pride more than any other, it is his sheer, stubborn, cussed, obstinate determination not to be shifted in his thoughts by the changing fashions of the day. Six weeks after that meeting with Kirkwood – as Scotland conclude a brief tour of continental Europe – he remains adamant that they are not going to the World Cup, which will kick off in late June; only a month away. The Scots win against France in the tour's final game and, later, during the post-match banquet at the Hotel Pavillon Henri IV in Saint Germain-en-Laye, Graham rises slowly to his feet, ready to deliver his speech to the hosts.

'Middens and Mon-sewers,' he says, turning with a nod and a smile to the French Football Association officials, 'I must thank you very much for your hostile . . . hospital . . . horse . . . pallity . . . Oh, you know what I mean . . . And I must also thank Mr Rémy Martin; is he in the building? No? Well, if you do see him, say that his little tipple went down a treat. Well, with me, anyway . . .

'Now, poor linguist as I am, I can still tell that all the talk here tonight is of only one subject: the World Cup. And, on that very subject, may I congratulate our French hosts in sharing with us and Portugal, our previous hosts on this tour, a very, very special hat trick – that of refusing to compete in this silly, new-fangled World Cup championship in South America.

'When we played England last month with the so-called "prize" of a berth at the World Cup riding on the match, it had the effect of relegating our annual encounter to the level of a cup tie and a foreign touch was conferred on that match that we would rather do without – if our hosts here don't mind me saying so.

'With all due respect to those present tonight, in the past few years we have seen players lusting after money in an open and a despicable way. This World Cup will, I'm sure, only make things worse. Look at what the Colombians are doing right now – they're stealing our very best players from under our noses. Two hundred Scottish players have regis-tered interest in switching to the Colombian League, tempted by signing fees of anywhere between £3,000 and £10,000 plus weekly wages rumoured to be anywhere between £120 and

£500 – and a swish, new home and a high-powered American car thrown in to boot. Prostitution it is! How can we protect our game, our Corinthian spirit, in the face of this blatant appeal to naked greed?

'Flavell of Hearts has gone to Colombia, spirited away like Cinderella at dead of night, coat over his head and on to an aeroplane: Jimmy Mason, Alec Forbes, Johnny Kelly, Jimmy Walker, Jimmy Docherty, the list of Scottish players who have been approached is just about endless . . . All of them were tempted away by one Joe Dodds – a former Scotland internationalist no less, but with a stronger siren voice than Anne Shelton and a man being paid, I am reliably informed, two hundred pounds for every player he can cart out of Scotland and into Colombia.

'Now, the upshot of it all is that the players' union in England – Colombia is poaching south of the border, too – is agitating for five-year contracts, with wages guaranteed at the same level throughout and at the end of which players would become free agents.

'Ridiculous! It's like a comic opera dreamed up by Bud Abbott and Lou Costello but it may mean the wrecking of our best club teams and our international sides too!

'Damned Tartars that they are!

'So all of this is what happens when faraway countries start to influence our game and I am sure this World Cup in Brazil will be the same. So it is a damn fine thing we are not going to it. No one abroad, it would seem, believes us when we say our sole reason for turning our back on the World Cup competition is principle . . . The general perception is that we are scared to go in case we find ourselves outmatched. Nothing could be further from the truth. These two tour matches – against Portugal and France – were

arranged specifically as warm-up encounters for the World
Cup in the event that we had been going but we finished
second in the Home Internationals so we don't go to Brazil.
That's the long and short of it and, I must say, it's the first
time I can see a lot of good having come from us finishing
second to England. We don't go to the World Cup. No! No!
No!'

As Graham settles unsteadily back into his seat, his face
flushed bright red, with an astonished silence emitting from
the assembled company, George Young, the Scotland captain,
rises to give his own speech of thanks. Discarding his prepared
notes, he pauses, and takes a long look at the SFA secretary.
'Mesdames and messieurs,' he begins, 'I have to thank you
all for proving such genial hosts, for laying on such a fine
banquet and for providing such demanding opposition in
today's match; one from which we were relieved and pleased
to emerge as victors.

'With the World Cup such a burning topic at this moment,
I feel that I must make mention of it. As the representative of
our Association, Mr Graham's words must be respected with
regard to their objectivity – it is, of course, probably neither
here nor there that we players are united in wanting to parti-
ipate in the World Cup. We probably don't know what is best
for us.

'Without further ado, and in recognition of our enjoyment
of this short tour, I would now like to make some presenta-
tions. To our kindly French hosts, I would ask that they do
us the honour of accepting this case of finest Scotch whisky
with which to remember us with fond and soothing thoughts.
For Alex Dowdells, our wonderful trainer, whose humour and
good nature have sustained us here on the continent, a set of
French boules – I know he is an enthusiast – and a bottle of

champagne, which I hope will go down well, too. For George Graham, our esteemed secretary, a suitcase. I know that while we players are not likely to be in Brazil this summer, Mr Graham has willingly accepted an invitation from FIFA to represent Scotland in an official capacity, and so I hope that Mr Graham will take this suitcase to Rio with him and that, every time he opens or closes it, he will think of my fellow team-mates and I who so wished to be with him but were denied that pretty opportunity.'

Spontaneous applause erupts throughout the room and Graham, suddenly wrenched into a moment of sharp sobriety, fixes Young with a cold, hard stare.

· 1950 · 1950 · 1950 · 1950 · 1950 · 1950 · 1950 · 1950 · 1950 · 1950 ·

'Champagne!' Robert Kirkwood shouts, half-turning his head toward a waiter as he settles into an elegant chair in the lounge of the Henri IV. Opposite him, George Graham, bleary-eyed, visibly brightens at the thought of a sparkling nightcap to revive his spirits following what he regards as Young's insubordination.

'I thought George Young made some good points,' Kirkwood says, folding a note into the appreciative waiter's hand as the bubbly arrives, 'and having mulled it over, and having witnessed the enthusiasm of the players to participate in the World Cup, I must inform you that we will, after all, be going to Brazil. I've spoken to Young about it and he tells me that the players will happily change holiday plans, etcetera, in order to play in South America.'

'The Scottish team will go to this World Cup over my dead

body!' exhorts Graham, causing a few heads to turn in surprise at his outburst.

Kirkwood gives a fresh cigar a couple of puffs to get it going, closes his lighter and replies, calmly, 'You know, old bean, you could not be more right. We will be going to the World Cup and if you continue to disagree with that, then you will be pretty much dead. I don't mean literally, of course, dear me, no, but figuratively you will be a dead duck. You see, I know all about the tickets.'

'What do you mean?' Graham interjects.

'What I mean is,' Kirkwood continues, maintaining his even tone, 'that I have been aware for some time of the discrepancy between the number of match tickets you release for sale to the general public and the number printed. I put two and two together, carried out investigations inside Carlton Place, and discovered that more than 6,000 out of the 134,000 tickets for the England match last month – tickets that were printed – were not passed on, by you, for general sale.

'I don't know what you did with them but I can guess . . . That's an awful lot of money for the Association to lose and for someone to use for the purpose of lining their own pockets. I've gone back over a few years and I see the same pattern for big matches – internationals, cup finals. Obviously, it has got to stop – and I'll say no more about it. Unless, that is, you refuse to see sense and reverse your decision not to attend the World Cup, where we can claw back some lost revenue. If you refuse, I shall send a telegram first thing tomorrow morning to Malcolm McCulloch, the chief constable, asking him to send some of his men to meet us at Abbotsinch airport when we step off the plane from France. I'm sure you'd be only too pleased to help them with any questions they may wish to ask you.'

The Dakota carrying the Scotland party circles above the great city of Rio de Janeiro, with Sugar Loaf Mountain jutting out above it majestically and Copacabana beach stretching seemingly into infinity. 'It's like fairyland in Technicolor,' shouts Scottish forward Billy Steel, to general amusement.

The Scotland players from the European tour remain in a general state of disbelief that they are here at all, as does Jimmy Mason, whose addition to the party was demanded by his team-mates because, as Hibernian striker Lawrie Reilly suggests, he is the type of player who makes it impossible for those around him to play badly. No one is in a greater state of shock than George Graham, even though it was he who, at the Henri IV on the morning after the banquet, had announced that Scotland would, after all, for the general benefit of the game and in response to the heartfelt pleas from associates abroad and, especially, at home, attend the finals of the World Cup.

Graham remains resentful at having been outmanoeuvred by Kirkwood but, as he cranes his neck to look down upon the carnival city and Copacabana beach, the players' excitement feeds through to him and he wonders whether there might not be something in this World Cup thing after all.

· 1950 · 1950 · 1950 · 1950 · 1950 · 1950 · 1950 · 1950 · 1950 · 1950 ·

'Unparalleled scenes greeted the England and Scotland squads when they stepped off their shared transatlantic flight to Rio de Janeiro today,' W. Capel Kirby, one of the few British pressmen to attend the World Cup, reports, in a story sent back to Britain on 20 June 1950.

> I arrived here on the same plane as our favourites and we found that this famous Brazilian city has gone quite haywire with football excitement. At the airport, pandemonium broke loose as we stepped from our plane and it seemed as if the English and Scottish boys' appearance was the signal to relieve the pent-up excitement of weeks of anticipation. There was every evidence that the sight of Billy Wright and his mates and George Young and the Scottish players had brought things to a climax but curiously enough, the fans of Rio are not thinking of England – or the Scots – winning the Cup. Brazil are favourites, with Uruguay mentioned as their closest rivals. The most favoured country from Europe is Spain. These Latins either know something we don't or they plain like to keep things local.

· 1950 · 1950 · 1950 · 1950 · 1950 · 1950 · 1950 · 1950 · 1950 · 1950 ·

Rio this June of 1950 is making Glasgow look as football-crazy as a Home Counties suburb. Every foreigner is accosted by groups of locals demanding to know where they come from and what they think of Brazil's chances of winning the tournament. Even the more wide-eyed among the visitors quickly realize that the best option is to smile and say 'Bra-zeeel!'

Down at the Copacabana Palace Hotel on Rio's seafront a rare sight is unfolding. George Graham is enjoying a break between the official pre-tournament referees' reception and a gathering of FIFA's international committee. Not only has the

15

SFA secretary, self-appointed bastion of propriety back home, divested himself of customary homburg, waistcoat and tie but he is, feet splayed, arms outstretched, attempting to mimic local dance moves in the wake of two young Brazilian ladies, tournament hostesses. This performance is taking place in the hotel ballroom, which is crowded with FIFA dignitaries, local football officials, journalists, translators, facilitators and administrators, all of whom are being attended to solicitously by an army of waiters offering an impressive array of refreshments.

'I've never had such a hectic day,' Graham – taking a break from the dance floor – confides to Swedish delegate, Lars Agelmo. 'I think I've met a representative of almost every nationality in the world and, to make sense of every conversation . . . Well—' Graham pauses to mop his dripping brow, 'I would have needed at least a dozen interpreters following my every step.'

'You seemed to be following well the steps of those delightful girls,' offers Agelmo with a grin. Graham, lost for words, merely gives a shake of the head and exhales heavily. 'I've never encountered anything like this in High Shawlands,' he says at last, to the bafflement of his Swedish acquaintance.

Sir Nigel Ronald, British ambassador to Brazil, saunters over to join the two men. 'I must say,' he tells Graham, 'I think your boys are a wonderful bunch. I've been chatting to them and I trust they will do the right thing and return a victory for Scotland – which would be, of course, a victory for Britain.'

· 1950 · 1950 · 1950 · 1950 · 1950 · 1950 · 1950 · 1950 · 1950 · 1950 ·

Two days prior to Scotland's opening match with Bolivia, two press men – Mr W. Capel-Kirby and Mr W. Gallagher – confer within the confines of the Adelmar da Costa Carvalho Stadium in Recife. They had been promised the Scotland team line-up at midday but that has come and gone and the reporters' deadline is fast approaching – they need to file the team lines today if British newspapers are to print them the day before the match.

When, eventually, the Scotland team and officials arrive, the two journalists bowl up and ask Graham for the line-up. 'Oh, we haven't got round to selecting it quite as yet,' Graham replies and, when informed of the press representatives' predicament, tells them to wait where they are, in the area at the mouth of the tunnel. 'Won't be a moment,' Graham says as he bustles over to Walter Johnstone, the selection committee chairman, and his co-selector John Park.

Johnstone, somewhat archly, raises an eyebrow in the direction of the reporters but he follows Graham and Park into the stand where they sit down and , then and there, cobble together the team for Scotland's first World Cup match. As the press men wait, trainer Alex Dowdells puts the players through their exercises on the pitch. Graham returns with a page torn out of a notebook and hands it over. 'Always happy to oblige and to help the press,' he says.

Capel-Kirby quickly files a report.

The turf here at the Adelmar da Costa Carvalho Stadium, Recife, is as soft on the feet as a Ritz Hotel floor covering, and Mr George Graham of the Scottish Football Association was in jocular mood as he anticipated with great relish Scotland's first steps on its well-kempt carpet of turf in this the World Cup of football nations. 'We can play top football on anything,' he told me, 'so we can play on this. Watch out Bolivia!'

The Bolivians themselves, though, are a confident
bunch. 'We will show that we are faster, fitter
and better fighters,' Mario Pretto, their Italian
team manager, told me this afternoon while watching
his team warm up on the turf shortly before the
Scots' arrival. 'We are like a New York pizza – we
have a little bit of everything to make a whole. I
saw Scotland play England and I have told my
players they have nothing to fear.'
It is enough to make any self-respecting Highlander
reach for his claymore but the Scots will need
cool and calculating heads if they are to defeat a
set of Bolivians on whose behalf I can vouch are
nimble, light and athletic.

· 1950 · 1950 · 1950 · 1950 · 1950 · 1950 · 1950 · 1950 · 1950 · 1950 ·

'Look at this – £51,000 was gathered in receipts from Brazil's first match,' Robert Kirkwood says to George Graham, who interestedly gazes at the FIFA news bulletin in Kirkwood's clutch. 'Fine, fine,' Graham says lightly – his first warm response to his fellow SFA man in weeks, his mood visibly lightening towards his colleague. 'I only hope some of it ends up in our pockets . . . I mean the coffers of the treasury, of course . . .' He steps away and heads off to have some final words with the Scotland players prior to the encounter with Bolivia.

There are twenty minutes remaining before kick-off when Graham enters the dressing room. Some players are fastening bootlaces and tieups for their socks; others are sitting still, nervously; Billy Steel, in stocking soles, is jogging on the spot; George Young, the captain, is going around the players administering quiet words of encouragement. In one corner of the room sits a dummy, built from spare tyres cut and shaped into a rotund figure, complete with round glasses, a pipe and with a whisky tumbler taped to its outstretched right arm. Graham looks at this entity with some suspicion.

'What's that?' he barks.

'It's our mascot,' the pawky Steel replies, 'a tubby wee guy who's with us everywhere we go. He's just a figure of fun. Know what I mean, Mr Secretary?'

Graham decides it is best to give the matter no further attention and, instead, to get on with the business in hand. 'Now, boys,' he says, standing in the middle of the dressing room, 'you've got a big game today and we all want to win it, don't we? Now, you've been doing very well. You have won eight out of your last ten matches . . .'

Steel interrupts, 'Aye, and it would have been ten out of ten if the bonuses had been bigger.' Laughter erupts, defusing some of the tension among the players.

'That's as maybe,' Graham says, stiffly. 'Just remember, you are representing Scotland so I want you all to play your parts, play up and do your very best and you should be more than a match for these Paraguayans.'

'It's Bolivia,' Bobby Evans reminds him gently.

'What, what?' Graham asks.

'We're playing Bolivia, sir, not Paraguay.'

'Yes yes, very well, Bolivia.' Graham turns on his heel and exits the dressing room, muttering to himself, 'Paraguay, Uruguay, Peru-uguay, Pe-livia, what's the difference?' More relaxed laughter spreads among the players.

'Just give me the ball when we get out there,' Billy Steel tells his team-mates, 'and I'll tear them apart.'

There are 9,841 curious locals inside the stadium in Recife as Bolivia and Scotland take the turf on Sunday 25 June

1950; the debut appearance for both nations in a World Cup finals. The Adelmar da Costa Carvalho is a far cry from Rio's brand new Maracanã, which the Scots visited shortly after their arrival in Rio only to find thousands of workers clambering all over the enormous new structure in a desperate attempt to make it ready for the start of the tournament. Recife is different; the local club's basic ground having simply been coopted as a match venue with no frills attached.

There are cylinders of oxygen on standby on the sidelines as the temperature nudges 30 degrees (86°F) at the early-afternoon kick-off time and the Bolivians spring into action, clicking and whirring with precision and shuttling the ball around swiftly. Celestino Algarañaz, after five minutes, eases inside from the right wing and deceives Sammy Cox with one shimmy and George Young with another before whipping in a shot that tickles the toes of Jimmy Cowan's left-hand post.

Only dogged defending protects the Scots' goal throughout the first half as they find themselves second best to the Bolivians' incisive passing – there are few chinks to be found in the Iron Curtain defence that has been transposed so successfully from the powerful Rangers side to the national team. Overwhelmed by a draining combination of the searing heat and their heavy, unsuitable kit, the more creative Scots are not in the game but the Scots manage to reach half-time with the score still 0–0.

In the dressing room, Graham looks intently at the five-man forward line: Bobby Campbell, Allan Brown, Lawrie Reilly, Billy Steel and Billy Liddell. 'Things just are not working smoothly with the forward boys,' Graham announces.

Young, sucking on a lump of ice, looks at Graham. 'Maybe

they would have had a better chance of clicking,' he says sharply, 'if they'd had a chance to play together before today and you hadn't been chopping and changing the team around on a whim.'

A quietly seething Steel turns to Graham and asks the selector, 'Would you like a drink, Mr Graham, to help you concentrate on what we should do next? I've got a bottle of something called cachaça here that I was given by one of the Brazilian officials; it's supposed to be very nice. Will I pour you a wee dram to make you feel right at home?' Graham, despite the pressing matter of Scotland's World Cup tie, responds in the manner Steel had expected. 'Very kind of you, Steel,' he says in a mellow, grateful fashion, 'very kind of you, and, as you say, it will help me to relax and concentrate better while I decide how we can improve things for the second half.'

Steel pulls a bottle of golden liquid from his kitbag and unscrews the top with a click that Graham, eagerly awaiting his refreshment, finds hugely pleasing. He is surprised, then, when Steel turns to the 'mascot' in the corner and proceeds to fill its glass then, quickly, sets down the cachaça bottle, picks up the dummy and gets it between himself and Graham before using it to maneouevre the shocked secretary out of the door and into the corridor. Steel, then, locks the door from the inside.

Young now addresses his team-mates uninterrupted – other than by Graham's muffled yells and futile banging at the door.

'We should press up harder on their players in the middle of the park,' Young says. 'Allan and Steelie, you should play more advanced – that'll give you a better chance of getting the ball from the Bolivians before they can build up and it will save you energy. Billy Liddell and Bobby Campbell, I want you not to worry so much about getting to the goal-line and crossing. Instead, play it inside if that's on. We need to play these boys at their own game.'

Young's tactics work admirably. The guileful Bolivians discover that their attacks are cut off at source thanks to sharp tackling from the Scottish wing-halves, and the Scots' more withdrawn wingers are cutting down the supply of the ball to the opposition's own wide men. With the Bolivian attacking movements reduced to a trickle the Scots start to become a serious creative force for the first time in the match and, with sixty-six minutes gone, Lawrie Reilly picks up the ball midway inside the Bolivian half, veers inside and sends in a shot. It appears to be going wide until it takes a wild deflection off Brown's right leg, corkscrews up and over the head of the Bolivian keeper, Edmundo 'Chembo' Gutiérrez, and drops down into the net.

The Scots are now breathing all over their opponents and, twelve minutes later when a dilatory Alberto de Acha dwells on the ball on Bolivia's right, Liddell opportunistically robs him and sends a low, hard cross into the heart of the penalty area for Reilly to first-time the ball through the legs of Gutiérrez. The *coup de grâce* arrives with eight minutes remaining. Bolivia are throwing bodies forward in search of a goal when one of their attacks breaks down. Alec Forbes carries the ball half the length of the field and switches it to Billy Steel. The pass goes too wide for Steel to have a shot at goal so the inside-forward crosses, seeking out Reilly. The ball, again, goes long, away from Reilly, but is retrieved close to the goal-line by Forbes. When his more precise centre reaches Reilly, the centre-forward, under pressure from two Bolivian defenders, stretches to reach the ball and, using the sole of his boot, pushes a low shot into the corner of Gutiérrez's net to conclude the scoring in a 3–0 win for Scotland.

· 1950 · 1950 · 1950 · 1950 · 1950 · 1950 · 1950 · 1950 · 1950 · 1950 ·

It makes for a good start to Scotland's World Cup. Now, with France absent from their four-team group – after objecting to the potential costs and travelling involved to participate – the Scots have seven days to wait until their second fixture. They switch base from Recife to São Paulo where they will prepare for the forthcoming match against Uruguay in Belo Horizonte. The days in between the two games are taken up with sight-seeing and watching World Cup matches. The players become friendly with Harry Martin, an American professional tennis player who has set up home in Brazil. Martin owns a café in São Paulo and the free ice cream he presses upon the players whenever they visit is a much-talked-about treat among them and anticipation of their visits there helps to lighten their mood and make the time between matches pass pleasantly.

Only once does George Graham, still testy after the incident at half-time in the Bolivia match, join the Scotland players and officials at Martin's café. Intrigued by an ice cream fountain in the centre of the floor Graham lifts a spoon and moves in to scoop up a sample from the gently whirling contraption, only for his tie to become trapped in the machinery. The SFA secretary is soon being dragged awkwardly around the fountain, arms flailing and squealing with discomfort and embarrassment. Kirkwood intervenes and helps to free him but too late to prevent his colleague suffering a gooey ice cream coating. With his glasses spattered, hat soggy and and shirt soaked with the cold confection, Graham makes for the door.

'There's one guy who doesn't need any help to look like a Charlie,' Billy Steel shouts.

Graham was meant to hear the quip, and he did, but he

is in no condition to issue a rebuke. After Steel's insult to him in Recife Graham had been on the verge of sending Steel home for his actions at half-time in the Bolivia match but has been 'persuaded' not to do so by Kirkwood who has pointed out that Steel was a pivotal player in the team's victory and could be crucial to the team's chances of further progress. Kirkwood has stressed that the more matches the squad can play, the greater the financial rewards the SFA will reap.

The Scotland squad attend the Maracanã to see Brazil draw 2–2 with Switzerland – a result that throws into doubt the Brazilians' qualification for the next round and which sparks fury among the locals, who throw fireworks at the players and spill onto the pitch to confront them as they leave the field. The stadium is engulfed in plumes of yellow firework smoke and a nearby cannon is booming out. 'If they are the favourites,' Billy Steel says as the Brazilians leave the pitch, 'we've got nothing to worry about. Refresh my memory if I'm wrong but didn't we just beat the Swiss 3–1 at our place back in April?'

Up in Belo Horizonte, the following day, it is a more muted Scotland squad that leave the Independência Stadium after witnessing Uruguay thwack Bolivia 8–0, with four goals in each half and each of their five forwards hitting the target. The most notable aspect of the Uruguayans' game, other than their exquisite ball-playing skills, is their speed off the mark and swift support for one another. Their strips look light-weight in contrast to the Scots' heavy cotton ones, their boots like carpet slippers compared to those of the Scots which have stiff leather up above the ankle, a steel plate in the sole and a bulbous toecap – boots built neither for comfort nor for speed.

Three days later, in the Independência's dressing room,

Young gathers his players around him and suggests that they play the game cagily. Given the Uruguayans' impressive mobility he wants his team to play it tight. They do just that, with Young leading the way by winning every ball in the air until, in the thirty-first minute, Eusebio Tejera advances down the Urguayuan left wing and chips the ball forward. Willie Woodburn is caught under it, and Young is too far behind Juan Schiaffino who makes clever use of the space Young has allowed him. Schiaffino turns and reverses a pass in the direction of Omar Miguez, the centre-forward, who has dropped back to a spot just outside the Scottish penalty area. The ball bounces off Miguez's knee but his reflexes are too cute to allow that to hamper him and he quickly adjusts his body, stretches out a leg and sends a left-footed volley high into the top left-hand corner of the Scots' net.

Scotland remain in the game, gradually growing in confidence after half-time, with the Uruguayans becoming frustrated in the face of repulsion by the Scots' defence – and with ten minutes of the second half gone, the Scots' shot at glory arrives. Bobby Campbell's cross from the right wing is perfectly paced and placed for Willie Bauld, who has displaced Steel in the starting line-up.

Bauld had been shunned by the selectors since missing a golden chance against England in April but Steel is now completely out of favour with them after a late-night prank in which he loosened all the bolts and screws in Willie Woodburn's bed so that when the centre-half retired for the night, bolstered by a flotilla of beers, it collapsed under him with a crash that resonated throughout the hotel. Then there was a lot more noise when Woodburn, renowned for his short fuse, emerged from the room seeking vengeance on the miscreant who had set him up for a fall.

The selectors' disciplinary whim has been announced to the players just half an hour before kick-off, leaving them without the chance to appeal to Kirkwood, so Bauld, short of match practice, and Reilly have been left to work out how to play alongside each other when both are used to the centre-forward role. They have been getting in each other's way throughout the afternoon but now, ten minutes into the second half, Reilly hangs back as Bauld soars into the air. He is only two feet from goal and meets the cross only to contrive, somehow, to head the ball up from under the crossbar and over the target. Scotland fail to create such a gilded opportunity again and Uruguay hold on to win 1–0. The South Americans top the group and Scotland are out of their first World Cup finals.

· 1950 · 1950 · 1950 · 1950 · 1950 · 1950 · 1950 · 1950 · 1950 · 1950 ·

'It went as well as could be expected, don't you think?' Graham suggests to Kirkwood at the post-match reception. Both men are looking forward to a further fortnight in Brazil during which they expect to undertake some strenuous FIFA duties, such as enjoying fabulous hospitality and watching the remainder of the tournament. They are complacently happy that the team has participated, that their futures with FIFA seem secure and that a division of the profits from the World Cup will be on its way to Scotland. Their extended sojourn means, however, that Graham and Kirkwood will miss reading an article sent home by Jerry Dawson, an outstanding Scotland goalkeeper during the 1930s and '40s now turned newspaper columnist. Dawson has witnessed the Scots' efforts in this World Cup and his story is on the streets in Scotland three days after the Uruguay defeat:

> The foreigners must be complimented on realizing their weaknesses and on doing something about them while we have been content to jog along and hope that our traditional football would pull us through. Now that tradition has so obviously let us down, will we be content to accept our relegated position among the football nations or will the powers-that-be appoint international team managers and coaches to instil some method into the selecting and blending of our future representative elevens?
> In the face of the skilled and organized opposition now to be met, I reckon that the old methods of selecting a team on individual merit, without thought as to whether or not it will dovetail, are past.

Only time will tell whether Dawson's views or the self-serving complacency of the selectors in maintaining their control over team matters will prevail during the four-year period prior to the next World Cup. Either way, participation in the 1954 event – in Switzerland – has become a 'must' for Scotland: the players who travelled to the World Cup in Brazil have been captivated by the sights, sounds, style and thrill of it all.

Switzerland in 1954 will be cooler and closer to home and that, they feel, will allow them a better tilt at the trophy. Midway through the 20th century it is clear that, thanks to the World Cup, the landscape of the game of football is changing rapidly. The Scots' approach to the next World Cup will determine whether they are to become a mere pock mark scratched on the tournament's surface or one of the Cup's most distinguished landmarks.

1954

JUST ABOUT MANAGING

An instinctive and generous round of applause breaks out and ripples around the terraces at the St Jakob Stadium in Basle within thirty seconds of the start of Scotland's match with Uruguay. Uruguayan defender José Santamaria pauses, hovering on the ball, to see what all the fuss is about but from his position deep in the Uruguay half can discern nothing and so he knocks the ball back to Roque Máspoli, his goalkeeper, who picks up the ball and stands bouncing it up and down as he scans the stands and pitch but he, too, is unable to figure out why this unexpected tumult of appreciation is pouring down from the 43,000 Swiss spectators.

Though no Scot has yet touched the ball, it is the Scottish players the Swiss crowd is applauding. On the pitch at St

Jakob the Scots are enacting something close to a choreo-graphed tribute to the host nation.

At kick-off, the Scots had set themselves out in the tradi-tional, British 2–3–5 formation but that all changed within the first thirty seconds: Jimmy Davidson, the centre-half, remains in a central position in midfield while Tommy Docherty and Doug Cowie, the half-backs, retreat from the middle of the field to go inside Willie Cunningham and John Aird, the full-backs. No Scottish team has ever before embraced this format – it is a clear approximation of the revolutionary 'Swiss bolt' system – that nation's pride and joy – hallmarked and honed during the postwar years by the host nation's footballers.

The eight Scottish pipers who entertained the crowd pre-match had, also, been rapturously received. The Swiss have been impressed by the Scots' showing in their 1–0 victory over Austria – being neighbouring countries Austria and Switzerland are, naturally, sporting rivals. Over and above this, the Swiss have been upset by a newspaper report of a casual remark made about them by Tom Finney, the England player, and the Scots have benefited enormously in being seen here as the 'other side of the coin' from the English.

Finney's casual observations regarding his hosts had been overheard by a Swiss newspaper reporter and duly publicised:

```
The locals appear to be considerably more inter-
ested in climbing up and down their mountains,
eating funny little triangle-shaped bars of choco-
late and explaining why their clocks are so much
better than any others in the world than worrying
about this great tournament that has landed on
their doorstep.
```

The progenitor of the new Scottish formation – the first time a Scottish team has deviated from the traditional 2–3–5 in eight decades – is Andy Beattie, Scotland's first ever manager, appointed in February 1954 specifically to help the team qualify for this tournament.

The weather is cool this June of 1954 – several showers having doused the city prior to kick-off – and Uruguay, world champions, cannot pierce the near-watertight Scottish defence. Long before the final whistle the side that bested Brazil to take the trophy in 1950 appear to have settled for the 0–0 draw that will see both themselves and Scotland advance from their group to the quarter-finals but in the dying minutes, the Scots create a flurry of action in and around the Uruguayan penalty area and, after Willie Ormond has gone close, the ball falls to Lawrie Reilly positioned centrally and fifteen yards from goal. Reilly is temporarily unattended but his shot flies over the crossbar. Hands clutching head, the player almost immediately hears the final whistle sounded by Italian referee Vincenzo Orlandini. It says much for the high expectations and morale of the Scots that it is disappointment at failing to beat the champions, rather than pleasure at holding them, that registers on the players' faces as they return to the dressing room.

'I first saw this style of play used when the Swiss visited Hampden Park a few years ago,' Beattie says afterwards – he is beaming, having achieved a place in the next round. 'I thought I'd keep it under my hat until we needed it in the World Cup. If you try to attack a team like Uruguay nonstop you are sure to come a cropper, so I did what I thought was best – and we nearly stole a win from under their noses at the end, didn't we?

'This triumph affords me greater pleasure than anything

else that I've achieved in my career to date. Just think, before we left home, people there were saying that a 1–0 defeat to the Austrians, one of the teams principially favoured to win the tournament, would be a triumph in itself, and our own people hardly dared contemplate what might happen to us against Uruguay who, if anything, are even stronger now than when they won the Cup four years ago.

'I'm happy, happy as can be, but I won't be resting on my laurels, no sir. My next task is to ascertain the fitness and frame of mind of all of our chaps and as soon as I've done that, I shall be scooting off to Berne to watch our friends England and Switzerland contest the match that I believe will likely throw up our next opponents.'

With a huge smile transfixing his face, Beattie looks dapper in his official Scotland squad blazer and he links his hands casually behind his back as he takes his leave of the half-a-dozen reporters gathered before him to scribble their notes in a slightly fusty-smelling back room inside the St Jakob Stadium.

The Scottish party take a fleet of taxis to Basle's Grand Hotel for the post-match banquet. As they draw up at the hotel a crowd of Scottish supporters are passing by on the pavement. Bedecked in tartan scarves and tammies, they are shouting and singing the praises of Lawrie Reilly but when the player himself steps out of his taxi, the supporters fail to recognize their hero and walk right past him – such are the innocent delights of this era, one upon which television has barely intruded, and during which footballers are photographed rarely. Fans see players from the terraces and stands and recognize them by their strip and style of play – out of the context of the game players often go unheeded by supporters.

While Beattie could hardly be happier, not everyone associated with the Scotland squad is feeling that way. Back at the team's hotel, Beattie is bouncing up the stairs to pack a bag for his trip to Berne when he is assailed by Tam Reid, one of the three SFA team selectors. 'Word wi' you pal!' Reid yells, clicking his fingers and pointing towards a room off the reception area. Scotland's manager, an equable type, follows Reid into the room to find Bob Cook, another team selector, sitting with George Graham, the SFA secretary. Any niceties are waived as Graham barks at Beattie, 'What did you think you were playing at back there?'

'What do you mean?' Beattie asks.

'You know fine well what I mean,' Graham snaps, 'I mean putting a Scottish team out on a football park to play like that. We don't play that way. I've never seen anything so disgraceful in all my life. We selectors picked a team to play the Scottish way – *attacking* the other team – but you told them to sit tight, to sit it out. I suppose you think you're smart, eh?'

Beattie ponders this. The game of football has favoured him with a good living since he left the Aberdeenshire football club Inverurie Loco Works, to join England's Preston North End at the age of twenty-one – the move sparing him from a life working in agriculture or, perhaps, in the locomotive works after which his former club is named.

He has found football management suitable to his cerebral approach to life. As one of a new type of postwar manager in English football – who take a more considered approach to the game – Beattie has achieved success by studying variations in how the game is played and by employing gentle encouragement and a more friendly approach to gain the best from his players, albeit within a still-tight disciplinary framework. At Huddersfield Town, where he has been manager since 1952, the formula has worked beautifully for him, winning the club promotion in his first full season as their manager and, in the recent 1953–54 season, third place in England's top division.

Working with the Scotland squad, Beattie has found it difficult to deal with the overbearing, abrasive selectors – Graham, Reid and Cook – but he has kept those feelings, diplomatically, to himself. Beattie is still pondering over George Graham's concerns when Reid interjects, 'Look, pal, you've been getting above your station. Your job is to oversee the players, not to put a load of fancy notions in their heads.

'If Sir George is the headmaster, you're the janitor. So you remember that. In the scheme of things you are just one notch above the trainer. We chose that team to play the game the way we want to see it played. It's not your job to change it all around and make it higgledy-piggledy so that no one can tell who is a defender and who is a forward. Bloody ridiculous!'

Reid is a bony man with a long, stern face and as he speaks his head bobs from side to side. He is wearing – because he has forgotten to take it off – a Tyrolean hat, a present from the Austrian FA, and as he admonishes Beattie the pointed headpiece, complete with feather, sways comically from side to side atop his cranium; Beattie can't suppress a smile from his lips and this only adds to Reid's fury.

Beattie's levity is only momentary and regaining seriousness, he tells his assailants, 'Mr Reid, Mr Graham, Mr Cook: I put the team on the field to get us into the next round of the World Cup; I believe that is my principal task. If I had set up the team to attack – as you suggest – in the Uruguay game, then I am certain we would have been given a thrashing. I have nothing further to say on the matter and am unwilling to discuss in any detail with you how I instruct the team in this tournament.'

Graham and Cook gasp and gape at each other and Reid's bulbous nose turns red.

'Since you have raised the matter,' Beattie continues. 'I feel now is a proper time for me to bring to your attention some of my own concerns.

'I propose that from now on in this World Cup I am given a free hand in how I deal with the team tactically. Not only that but I also wish to pick the team – with respect, I feel I am better suited to that task than you are. You have used twenty-seven players in four internationals this season and that's no way to get a settled team; I want eleven players working together, like a club side.

'Furthermore, Mr Reid has described my work as "ridiculous" when, in fact, the most ridiculous decision we have had to contend with – and made at the insistence of Mr Reid and Mr Graham – was to bring only thirteen players to this World Cup while every other country has a full squad of twenty-two. In the run-up to the tournament when I visited Vienna to watch Austria play Hungary, I told Walter Rausch, Austria's coach, that we were taking only thirteen men and he laughed. He refused to believe I wasn't joking.

'You told me, Mr Graham, that the Association could not afford the cost of taking to Switzerland any more than the thirteen players you had named. As a man of honour, I accepted that fact. I even felt sympathetic toward your plea that financial constraints restricted the size of the squad we could bring with us: but that changed when I boarded our aeroplane at Prestwick and found ten committeemen and their wives sitting on the plane, ready to fly out for a two-week, World Cup knees-up at the SFA's expense. At that time, I decided to keep quiet about it but now I must express my dissatisfaction.

'We've only got one goalkeeper with us! One goalkeeper,

Fred Martin – what happens if he gets injured? Have you thought about that? Now we're in the quarter-finals I must insist on having six more players flown out immediately. I've made it easy for you; I have a list of the players I want and it's right here in my jacket pocket.'

Graham sits agog in his ornate, cushioned hotel chair. The whisky he's almost forgotten he's holding spills from the glass on to the throne-like chair he chose, originally, for effect. 'Are you out of your mind, sir?' he splutters, once he has found his voice again. 'Do you really think that we will accede to all these outrageous requests just at a snap of your fingers? Just you remember who put you where you are, and I can send you packing, too.'

'I must inform you,' Beattie replies, 'that if you fail to agree to my terms, then I must immediately resign from my position as Scotland manager.'

'That's it, then,' Graham bawls. He stands up and thrusts his round face to within inches of Beattie's. 'That's it, sir. You jolly well resign, here and now, if that's how you wish to play it. I suggest you remove yourself to your room and pack your bags forthwith!'

Beattie turns and walks, dignity intact, from the room.

. 1954 . 1954 . 1954 . 1954 . 1954 . 1954 . 1954 . 1954 . 1954 . 1954 .

Two hours later, his bags duly packed, Beattie is in a taxi, hired by the SFA, on his way to Basle's central railway station. From here he expects to travel to Zurich where he is due to catch a hastily arranged flight home. The players are out and about in Basle, Beattie having allowed them off the leash to enjoy some time in Basle's city centre, including a visit to its prestigious zoo. They had not returned to the hotel by the time of Beattie's contretemps with the selectors so he scribbled an explanatory note and shoved it under team captain Willie Cunningham's bedroom door.

'Here am I, lonely on a rock, jutting out above the abyss,' Beattie muses as he stands on the station platform. He peers up at the station's imposing clock. The simplicity and clarity of its design, with each minute marked off by a straight line, in contrast to the more ornate, Victorian-type clocks back home reflects the progressive attitude of the Swiss, he observes – an attitude that Beattie has admired hugely during his stay in their country. A man open to new experiences, he will miss being at the World Cup but, being the balanced person he is, he is sanguine about it and, on recalling Tam Reid in that Tyrolean hat, a smile flickers across Beattie's face and words of a well-known song flash into his mind: 'Wherever I go they'd shout "Hello"/ Where did you get that hat?'

Five minutes before his train is due a flurry of activity at the far end of the platform attracts Beattie's attention – a boisterous group of men are disturbing the sedate, orderly Swiss on the platform who are spaced apart from one another as if by design. As the group draws closer Beattie realizes that it is the Scotland players: Willie Cunningham in the van, Tommy Docherty bustling along beside the captain, Jimmy Davidson with his loping stride and Fred Martin towering over the rest of them.

'Boss, boss, let me take your bag,' Cunningham says. 'We've got four taxis waiting outside and you know how much these Swiss boys charge so let's make a bit of haste here.'

'Wait a minute, Willie,' Beattie responds, 'don't you know that I've been sacked? I'm on my way home.'

'You're going nowhere,' the Scottish captain answers. 'Or if you do, we'll be going with you. We've told Graham and the others that, in no uncertain terms. Plus, I spoke to Mr Kirkwood and he'll back you against Graham and the rest of them if they try to make any more trouble.'

'I don't know what to say, boys. I'm touched, I really am. I never wanted to turn my back on this World Cup, or on any of you so, if you're with me, I'm with you.'

. 1954 . 1954 . 1954 . 1954 . 1954 . 1954 . 1954 . 1954 . 1954 . 1954 .

It proves to be the Swiss whom Scotland are to face in the quarter-finals; the hosts showing their quality by defeating Italy in a play-off to reach the last eight. Now what is to happen? Are both sides to use the 'Swiss bolt' and, if so, will this lock up the game?

There are 32,000 home supporters in the Olympique de la Pontaise Stadium, Lausanne, as the teams take to the field on a hot afternoon and the locals' reputation for neutrality is in severe jeopardy. Their team's unexpected success in defeating the Italians – twice inside a week – and in holding England to a draw has whipped them into a fever of nationalism that has raised concern among the country's ultra-cautious polit-ical commentators, who worry that this temporary insanity may have long-term damaging effects on the prosperously buttoned-up burghers of Switzerland.

Wave upon wave of tiny red flags with white crosses colour the terraces as the Scots and Swiss trot out on to the turf. On Lake Geneva's far shore the Alps form a stunning backdrop to the spanking-new stadium – a contemporary design with, like St Jakob, cantilevered roofs providing shade for the spectators behind both touchlines.

The Swiss immediately fan out into their 'bolt' formation – it is drilled into them – and so do the Scots; Beattie is keen for his team to be cagey in the opening stages. Some gentle sparring ensues but after sixteen minutes Charly Antenen swings a corner into the heart of the Scots' penalty area. The ball brushes the top of centre-forward Josef Hügi's head as it travels out to the left-wing then Jacky Fatton swiftly plays it back toward Hügi, who turns and slips a low shot past Fred Martin. Bedlam ensues as the Swiss convince themselves that they have drawn a step closer to clinching the World Cup.

Two minutes later, another Swiss corner; Fatton finds Olivier Eggimann rising to poke a simple header from the edge of the six-yard box inside Martin's right-hand post. The Swiss supporters are still in the process of rousing themselves into an even greater state of delirium over Eggimann's goal when a quick pass from Antenen, deep inside his own half, sets Hügi free, and with his second touch he drives the ball past the outcoming Martin to put the Swiss 3–0 ahead with fewer than twenty minutes played. Cue bedlam, plus plus plus.

As the Swiss players milk the response of the home crowd, Beattie leaves his seat in the directors' box, sprints down the stand's internal stairs and rushes down the players' tunnel and on to the touchline. Calling a despondent Cunningham to him, the manager instructs his captain to abandon 'the bolt' formation. 'They're much better at it than us,' Beattie tells his player. 'Concentrate on the quick-passing game we've been working on in training.'

Cunningham passes on Beattie's instructions as the Swiss, having milked their fans' applause, finally regroup ready for kick-off. The change of tactic peps up the Scottish players. Freed from the constraints of the safety-first 'bolt', they switch to a style of play much more in the Scottish tradition – the style their great-grandfathers adopted in the game's earliest days – shuttling the ball around to feet, swiftly and skilfully. It feels to each and every one of them as if they are returning home to a well-worn pair of favourite slippers after attending a grand occasion in stiff, formal wear. Midway through the first half, the Scots' patient passing pays off when Willie Fernie finds Allan Brown in the middle of the park and he takes a touch before sending a sharp, accurate ball into the heart of the Swiss penalty area. It lands at the feet of Neilly Mochan, who pings a first-time shot past Eugene Parlier in the Swiss goal.

'Move the ball along the ground. It won't hurt the grass if we move the ball along the ground,' Beattie exhorts as his team reassembles for the kick-off. That their manager is talking to them from the touchline – a practice previously alien to the Scottish national team – boosts the players still more. Swiftly from kick-off the Swiss are dispossessed and Johnny McKenzie exchanges passes with Fernie, then Brown, before playing the ball to Mochan who rolls it between two Swiss defenders, bodyswerves around them as they close in for a 'sandwich' then manoeuvres himself and the ball away from another two Swiss before shooting past Parlier while simultaneously falling backwards.

After Mochan's goal the Scots hungrily await the restart. 'We want to make life easy for the groundsman, now,' shouts Beattie. 'Keep the ball on the grass and we'll save him a lot of work. We'll trim the grass with our passing.' Again, the Scots, eager and revived, swiftly rob the Swiss of possession and another close-passing move sends Fernie in on goal. He's confronted, at an angle, by Parlier but the Scottish inside-forward spots Mochan bursting into the middle. Fernie squares the ball and the centre-forward slaps it into the unguarded Swiss net to make it 3–3.

Gloomy faces now abound in the crowd; faces with expressions as cold as a roaring fire that has suddenly been doused in the grate; faces whose settled melancholy fills their fellow fans with profound depression; dreary, long, heavy countenances, empty of expression, with sad, pathetic, unseeing eyes. The torpor affects the entire crowd, Swiss almost to a man and woman and all, young and old, now share a look of pale-faced pusillanimity and pessimism – only a few minutes earlier, they had been in rapture. A hush has descended so that as Beattie, again, dashes to the touchline before the seventh kick-off in a match less than half an hour old, his exhortations can be heard clearly. 'Keep the high balls low,' he shouts, hands cupped around his face, 'and remember that if you find yourself in the eighteen-yard box and you've no one to give it to, just stick it in the net!'

There is almost a hiatus before Scotland's next goal – a whole four minutes pass before they, again, hit the Swiss net. This time McKenzie flights in a cross from the right and Brown's angled, close-range header gives Parlier no chance. Two minutes on, Doug Cowie heads down a McKenzie corner and Willie Ormond twists to flick an eight-yard shot high into the Swiss net. The Swiss get one back two minutes later when Robert Ballaman sweeps a sweet, accurately judged, twenty-yard, left-footed volley high past Martin. At half-time the score-line is an incredible 5–4 to Scotland – and this from two teams who had been expected to stage a defensive stalemate of a match.

At the interval, Beattie, who encourages his players so

successfully and publicly from the touchline, is to be found queuing anonymously at a tea bar underneath the main stand. As with players in this era, managers can move around in public with their privacy guaranteed. There are dual reasons for his seeking to steer clear of the dressing room. As a progressive manager he has never been one for saying too much at half-time in any match. He recalls his own playing career and how, with the players' concentration levels high, the manager's presence was an unwanted distraction and a hindrance rather than a help. He and his team-mates would see the manager's mouth moving and not hear the words. He also wishes to avoid George Graham. Despite the scoreline, Beattie knows that Graham will be furious with him. In the SFA secretary's opinion it is simply not done – and bad sport – for managers to attempt to influence a match from the touchline. The last thing Beattie needs is an argument with Graham in front of the players at such a vital stage in this afternoon's encounter.

None of the downcast Swiss, chewing cigarettes in a comradely fug of smoke and mumbling disconsolately about the half-time score in a language incomprehensible to Beattie, recognize the Scotland manager but a Scottish reporter does and happily ambles over to greet him with words of congratulation.

'The game's only half over,' responds Beattie with professional caution. The journalist laughs then says, 'Oh, you might be interested in this . . . The Swiss FA have put out a press release stating that all goals scored against Switzerland in the first half were owing to the sun.' Beattie glances at the press release, chuckles and slips back up the tunnel just as the referee rings the bell for the players to take the field for the second half.

'You're doing great, boys,' Beattie tells his team, as he gathers them around him before they take to the turf, 'but the

Swiss are saying that the only reason you scored any goals is because the sun was in the goalie's eyes.' A swell of dissent rises from his men. 'Thought you might be interested in that,' Beattie says, smiling.

Nine minutes after the interval, McKenzie, on the halfway line, sends the ball ten yards forward to Tommy Docherty, who pushes the ball forward another ten yards or so to Brown who, first time and just before André Neury arrives ready to administer a thumping tackle, clips it across to Ormond. When Neury then chases down Ormond, the Scots' winger sends a reverse pass to Brown who immediately nudges the ball on to Mochan, who spreads it across to Fernie who makes as if to shoot but, instead, flicks the ball to the side and directly into the path of the inrushing McKenzie and it is he who sends a stunning twenty-yard, diagonal shot past Parlier for the Scots' sixth.

That goal – on an afternoon on which the temperature reaches a peak of thirty-two degrees centigrade – is not only a product of scientific soccer but also of scientific preparation. Unlike in the 1950 World Cup the Scots are, this time, kitted out in lightweight Aertex shirts plus nylon, mid-thigh-length shorts and soft leather Rio boots weighing only ten ounces. Beattie's thoroughness has extended to gathering information from those players who participated in the Brazil World Cup. They told him they had been disadvantaged by cumbersome clothing and boots so he, therefore, provided loose, lightweight kit to suit the often balmy Swiss summer. Appropriately equipped, the Scots in '54 have played like men released from their shackles.

'Fail to prepare – prepare to fail' is just one of the Scottish manager's slogans but one he saw fit to have incorporated into the specially designed key rings issued to every squad member. His meticulous preparations for the Swiss match have paid off. One of the most dramatic matches in World Cup history concludes at 6–4 in Scotland's favour.

. 1954 . 1954 . 1954 . 1954 . 1954 . 1954 . 1954 . 1954 . 1954 . 1954 .

The following morning Beattie and his players are on the training pitch at half past nine. 'We spent a couple of hours afterwards applauding ourselves – and then we got back to work,' Beattie tells a Swiss reporter who has come to discuss the previous day's match. 'The spirit of the whole eleven is something of which we can be very proud.'

The Scots spend half an hour of the morning session practising trapping the ball under the foot, the next half hour on making runs on the blind side of a defence and the concluding hour honing their short-passing skills by working in pairs.

Beattie's is coaching of a type that few of these players have experienced, even though they are all with top-flight British clubs. As good, thinking footballers, they are receptive to their new manager's methods and have thoroughly enjoyed working with him since early May when they began pre-World Cup training. His frequently repeated aphorisms stick in the players' minds and, when recalled during a match they can trigger positive action. 'If you don't shoot, you won't score,' Beattie tells them as they prepare for the semi-final with West Germany. The rivals will meet at the St Jakob Stadium on 30 June.

Meanwhile, Tam Reid is at the team hotel addressing a gaggle of reporters with his own particular brand of logic. 'Our forwards have been instructed to go all out for an early goal,' he says of the forthcoming match, 'because we know from experience that the continentals don't like having to fight back. Special emphasis has been laid on the necessity of hard – but always fair – tackling. This should knock some of the funny notions out of the heads of the Germans. Our boys are rarin' to go. They have found a fine old confidence in themselves and, take it from me, they are not in the least worried about the much ballyhooed opposition.'

George Graham lacks Reid's confidence in the team, despite Scotland having reached the semi-finals of the World Cup, and – privately – he wants to see the back of Beattie. He felt compelled to apologize to his counterpart in the Swiss FA for the manager's touchline interventions, which Graham describes, even to the Swiss, as cheating. He is, also, still fuming about the assertive stance Beattie has taken regarding the team and at his disappearance at half-time in the match with Switzerland. Graham, privately, has decided that Beattie will be sacked as Scotland manager as soon as the World Cup is over, and if the players don't like it and threaten to rebel he will simply draft in a new lot for future internationals. Beattie is too clever not to be aware that his job is likely to be in jeopardy when this World Cup ends but he tidies his mind of such distractions and concentrates on the task in hand.

For all his willingness to embrace modern, scientific coaching methods and to face up bravely to bullying administrators, another facet of his character would surprise those who see him as a young, thrusting, modern manager. Beattie is a hugely superstitious individual and observes a number of rituals on match days. On the morning of 30 June, the date of the match with West Germany, he thrusts, as is his custom, a lucky acorn into his pocket. Beattie, on visiting Sherwood Forest two years previously, had scooped it up after it had fallen from a tree said to bring good luck and his Huddersfield team had gone on to beat Nottingham Forest that afternoon en route to winning promotion. Taking his raincoat from its hanger, he turns it inside out before putting it on – as he always does on match days. For the solitary morning walk he takes before every fixture Beattie wears his left shoe on his right foot and vice versa – the discomfort forces him, he feels, to keep complacency at bay.

Those and several other rituals carried out at intervals prior to kick-off ensure that time shuttles along swiftly for Beattie before the match with West Germany. This time, the Swiss will be rooting for the Scots, though there will be a hefty contingent of opposition supporters shouting for their favourites.

The West Germans prove to be more of a handful for the Scotland side than any of their previous opponents in the tournament. Hans Schafer cuts in from the left wing to administer the first blow after a quarter of an hour's play, tapping in Fritz Walter's cross after the inside-forward had deceived the Scots defence by temporarily displacing Schafer. It is the only goal of the first half but the West Germans are clearly the dominant side.

On a soggy surface inside the St Jakob stadium, the Scots' rivals have a huge advantage courtesy of a new innovation – screw-in studs; the Scots, minus that advantage, are finding conditions much more treacherous. Developed by the German boot manufacturer Adi Dassler and worn exclusively by the West German team, these screw-in studs are being pioneered at this World Cup and occasionally a German trots over to the touchline to have a loose stud adjusted by a special spanner. George Graham utters not a word about cheating to his West German counterpart and receives no apology from the West

Germans for gaining an advantage in this manner; embracing progress comes more easily to some than to others.

Two minutes after the interval Max Morlock climbs to head home Fritz Walter's cross after Fred Martin, having his poorest game of the tournament, has remained rooted to his line. 'Fred was like a crocus,' Tommy Docherty will say, later. 'He only came out once a year.'

Docherty himself brings down Schafer on the hour and when Walter puts away the penalty Scotland know their luck has run out. Beattie removes his raincoat to turn it the right way around. As the teams stand to attention at the end of the game to hear *Deutschland über Alles* and *God Save the Queen* with the West Germans 3–0 victors, Andy Beattie is hit hard by the realization that after the experience of this World Cup his life will never be quite the same again. He is looking forward to returning home to his semi-detached house in a respectable part of Huddersfield, his neighbours either side a bank manager and a civil servant, but as his eyes alight on a nearby tournament poster featuring a football as an illuminated globe, he realises that a little bit of light has gone out in his own world.

TALKING A GOOD GAME

'Hello. My name is Dawson Walker. Eh, well, my work
. . . you want to know about my work? Right, well, I am the
trainer at Clyde, the fitba' club that plays at Shawfield Stadium,
you know, where the dugs run on a Saturday night. What are
my duties? Well, kind of what you would expect, you know.
I'm the trainer. Every club's got one.

'You want to know exactly what I do? Right, right. Well, I
kind of do everything that involves looking after the players.
So I take them through their exercise routines – basically that
means I just get them on the running track and make sure there's
no slacking for the next couple of hours. See some of them,
they're so bone idle, if I had my way they'd be put on the track
on race night as a replacement for the hare and I'd take off the

dugs' muzzles – that'd get the lazy beggars moving . . . Anyways, I do that and then if any of them need a wee rub down after training, I get out the olive oil. I know a lot about muscles and bones just through being here all these years. I also repair the boots – a wee bit of a cobbler I am, too.

'What else do I do? Oh yes, on the first Tuesday of every month I make the players drink a tumbler-full of cascara sagrada – it doesn't smell very nice and they don't like it but it gets their bowels moving, ha ha – and, before a match, it's me that gets out the boots and strips and lays them out properly at each man's peg, and if any of them need strapping, maybe on an ankle, I'll do that too. Also, any time one of their wives has a baby, I put together a wee box full of stuff like baby powder, rattles, things like that. If a player needs extra treatment on an injury, they can come to my house, where I've got all the physiotherapy equipment. Oh and as well as all that, if I've got any spare time I sometimes help out the groundsman by rolling the pitch.

'So, as you can see, I'm kept pretty busy and I suppose I'm very proud of the work I do here. I feel I can turn my hand to most things but I have to admit I'm a bit bamboozled by what I've been asked to do for my next job, in fact I wouldn't know where to start with it: that is, the Scottish Football Association want me to be the manager of the Scotland team at the World Cup in Sweden in June . . . Now, if you want to know what that's all about, don't ask me . . .'

· 1958 · 1958 · 1958 · 1958 · 1958 · 1958 · 1958 · 1958 · 1958 · 1958 ·

A letter drops on to the thick doormat of the Scottish Football Association in the middle of this April of 1958. Addressed to

Willie Allan, the secretary of the SFA, it emanates from Matt
Busby at Old Trafford, Manchester.

Dear Mr Allan,
I hope this missive finds you well.
    Thank you for the telegram conveying your
felicitations. My recovery after the crash at
Munich is continuing to go as well as could be
expected. However, as I believe Les Olive, our
club secretary, intimated to you on the telephone,
I shall be unable to accompany the Scotland team
as manager at the World Cup in Sweden this summer.
I had hoped to persuade my physicians otherwise
but they are most insistent that over the summer I
must rest as much as possible. So that's it, I'm
afraid.
    I remain most grateful to you for extending the
kind invitation to me back in January, shortly
before the draw for the World Cup tournament, to
manage the team in Sweden and, as a mark of that
gratitude, I would like to extend to you an invitation to accept the hospitality of my wife and
myself here in Manchester on the weekend after
next and to be my guest at the match with
Wolverhampton Wanderers.
    I look forward to hearing from you.
    Yours sincerely,
    Matt Busby
    Manager, Manchester United Football Club

· 1958 · 1958 · 1958 · 1958 · 1958 · 1958 · 1958 · 1958 · 1958 · 1958 ·

A fortnight later, Willie Allan – feeling amply relaxed – is
sitting alongside Busby in the Manchester United manager's
olive-green Jensen coupé. Les Olive is at the wheel as it speeds

along Cheshire's country lanes in the direction of Wilmslow, where Busby and his wife Jean will host Allan for Sunday lunch before returning him to Piccadilly station and the train home. The SFA secretary, having enjoyed the best of board-room hospitality at the match the previous day and a night at the Opera House watching Arthur Askey perform, has been put at ease by Busby's geniality to such an extent that he is feeling like an old family friend. On the journey to Wilmslow Busby sits, impassive, in the back seat, while Allan chunters on about an illegal amateur league that he has discovered recently in Fife and the sharp, smart measures that he took to close it down. 'Is that so?' Busby says, affecting interest. 'You never know what people are going to try on, do you? You never know the minute.'

'My thoughts exactly, Matt, my feelings exactly,' Allan replies.

'Ah here we are,' Busby says as Olive slows the car and draws up outside Marston's Steak House, a whitewashed building with lattice windows and a thatched roof. 'Very nice, very nice,' Allan says, contemplating the exterior in admiration.

'Yes,' Busby says. 'I find it a pleasant little Sunday retreat, and a bit of a haven for me. Not too many people from the city have the means of getting out here so that means you are afforded a degree of privacy.'

Even so, as the Busby party make their way through the restaurant, where they are greeted effusively by the maître d', other diners – predominantly rich Manchester business-men and their wives – pause to take a look at the great man. Busby, as always, is dignified but not aloof and makes no acknowledgement of this interest other than to thank the occa-sional individual who briefly wishes him well. Instead, he concentrates on manoeuvring his way delicately in the direction of a secluded table to the restaurant's rear. Busby is still using walking sticks as a result of the injuries he sustained in the Munich Disaster eleven weeks ago and now and then a twinge of pain will force him to wince but, keen not to discomfit those in his company, he swiftly shrugs off such moments.

With the meal over, Allan chooses a cigar from the box offered to him by the waiter and, as Busby tamps down the tobacco in his pipe, Les Olive and Jean Busby decide to take a constitutional around the nearby duck pond. Coffee, cheese and biscuits having been brought to the table, Busby relaxedly turns to Allan and in his mellifluous, hybrid Lanarkshire-Lancastrian burr tells him, 'I have to say, I appreciate you coming all the way from Glasgow to visit us, Willie – and giving up your weekend, too.

'It has been an honour for us to have the secretary of the Scottish Football Association among us. Having the pleasure of your company has made it all the more regrettable to me that I shall not be with you in Sweden this summer. I'm sure, though, that you will be providing me with a small honorarium for any advice I might give you in connection with the World Cup . . .'

Busby, who never forgets that it is a professional game in which he is involved, looks sideways at Allan, who is sitting deep in contemplation, and, knowing that his words are sinking in, the manager continues without waiting for an answer.

'Now, that brings me to the matter of the person you will choose to be my replacement at the World Cup in Sweden.' Busby, well-connected to the football community in Scotland, is fully aware that, in his absence, the SFA have a crazy plan to put Dawson Walker in charge of the squad but again he does not give Allan the chance to interject, instead continuing swiftly with his spiel. 'Now I know you will be giving thought to a whole number of people and will have some very good men in mind but since you're here, I was wondering whether you have thought about someone I have – in fact, I'm sure you've thought of him: Bill Shankly?'

Again Busby does not allow Allan any opportunity to answer. 'He is a young manager and he is doing very well at Huddersfield Town, as you well know. He's a man with a lot of good ideas about the game and he is a lively character – he would keep everyone on their toes out at the World Cup. He is also a most passionate Scot. If I were to nominate anyone – and I'm sure you don't need me to do so – but if I were, then he would be the man.'

Allan, a waspish stickler for rules and regulations, a ruthless defender of the proper way of doing things, a man who hardly allows anyone to draw breath inside the SFA unless the matter, like everything else, is approved by a committee, is not normally stuck for words. If it were anyone else than Busby he would tell him to mind his own business and not be so impertinent as to presume he might have such a say in an SFA matter. Instead, he ponders whether to tell Busby that he has opted to put Dawson Walker in charge of the team, only for the idea suddenly to seem rather ridiculous. Instead, luxuriating in his surroundings, the company, the cigar and the best cheddar and biscuits he has ever tasted, he follows the example of so many and merely nods his acquiescence in Busby's direction while inwardly resolving to do his own thing once back behind his desk in Glasgow.

'You see, Willie,' Busby goes on, 'all of the other countries at the World Cup will have a top manager with them; to make the most of this great occasion. The Germans will have Sepp Herberger, who won it for them the last time and who got a great deal of credit for making the difference between winning and losing. The Swedes have George Raynor, who took them to third place in the 1950 World Cup; Peter Doherty is to manage the Irish; Jimmy Murphy, my own assistant here, will manage Wales; Brazil have just appointed Vicente Feola. So we need, and I know you will agree, someone of prominence. I have every faith in you making the correct appointment.

'I will also be very keen to hear from your own lips just how the World Cup proceeded and would wish to take the first opportunity to do so. Therefore, I would like to extend an invitation to you to return here as soon as the World Cup is over – Manchester is a terrific place in the summer and we'll make sure we keep you entertained again. We'll have another great weekend and you can tell me in person just how our man got on as Scotland manager.'

· 1958 · 1958 · 1958 · 1958 · 1958 · 1958 · 1958 · 1958 · 1958 · 1958 ·

A 2–1 victory over Yugoslavia in Scotland's opening game of the 1958 World Cup is the talk of the tournament thanks to the winning goal. Denis Law, its scorer, is notable not only for being an eighteen-year-old winning his first cap but also for getting the goal with an overhead kick, a new technique alien to the British game and still rarely seen on the continent. Bill Shankly, in Sweden at the helm of the Scotland team, deserves the credit for audaciously naming Law in his squad and now, at a post-match press conference, Shankly tells his Swedish interpreter how to answer the array of questions being thrown at him by the journalists in attendance.

'With everything they say,' he says quietly in the interpreter's ear, 'just tell them I disagree and that I think the opposite,' is Shankly's quirky instruction and he revels in the confusion this sows in his inquisitors. The manager also insists that questions from the Scottish journalists be translated into Swedish before being answered. After a dozen minutes of this, Shankly abruptly leaves the press room without a word of farewell – he has other business to which he wishes to attend.

· 1958 · 1958 · 1958 · 1958 · 1958 · 1958 · 1958 · 1958 · 1958 · 1958 ·

'So are you going to give him the mortgage? Yes or no?' Shankly intones into the telephone in the lobby of the Grand Hotel, Norrköping, with Bill Brown, the Dundee goalkeeper, standing nervously in front of Shankly as the manager speaks long-distance to the manager of the building society with whom Brown wishes to arrange the purchase of his first house; a venture alien to a young man of working-class background. For months now, the player has been subject to dilly-dallying and delaying on the part of the self-important, puffed-up building society manager and Shankly, noticing that the player has been preoccupied during the early days with the Scotland squad in Sweden, has buttonholed Brown, discovered the problem, and is now attempting to resolve it in his own style. 'It is a simple question. Are you going to lend him the money?' is how he puts it to the money man. Five minutes later, Shankly replaces the receiver and tells Brown, 'That's it. You're the owner of a new home.' The player visibly relaxes and offers profuse thanks. 'If I call you into the team, that's when you can thank me,' Shankly says, to the accompaniment of his rasping, throaty laugh. Brown, who is yet to win his first cap, is in Sweden as backup to Tommy Younger, the long-established number one for the Scots.

· 1958 · 1958 · 1958 · 1958 · 1958 · 1958 · 1958 · 1958 · 1958 · 1958 ·

Prior to Scotland's next match, with Paraguay at the Idrottsparken, Norrköping, Shankly saunters up to the stadium's commissionaire, whom he has made a point of getting to know well over the previous couple of days. 'Kjell, when the Paraguayans arrive at the ground, I would like you to hand these to them and tell their coach, Mr Gonzalez, that I advise him to pass them out to his players before the kick-off.' He hands the burly Swede a sack containing two dozen toilet rolls and walks inside chuckling.

'Now listen boys,' he tells the players before they face the Paraguayans, 'you know that I don't really like to discuss the opposition before a match – never at all – but on this occa-sion I must make an exception because there is something that I really have to let you know about this Paraguay team.'

The rarity of Shankly dispensing a nugget of information about the opposition is enough to obtain rapt attention from his players, whose collective gaze is now unwaveringly fixed on their manager.

'I sent someone to watch them play against France,' Shankly continues, then pauses for effect before adding, 'and on the pitch, before the match, a number of them . . . put hairnets on.' Guffaws break out and relief seeps from players who had been concerned that their manager was about to give them some ominous news. 'Now, though I've mentioned it,' Shankly goes on, pleased to have relaxed his players with his words,

'I don't want you all to think these guys are a bunch of pansies. They are not. They're a tough little bunch of so-and-sos and they can dish out the rough stuff as good as anybody. I just didn't want you to be surprised at seeing them dealing with their hair before the game begins or to get the wrong impression from it.'

The Paraguayans live up to Shankly's words – they are indeed a combative bunch – but they are endowed equally with natty ball-playing skills and they are a serious match for the Scots. Shankly has introduced Tommy Docherty and Dave Mackay to the team specifically for this game, players who combine skill and substance in the middle of the park. The presence of Law in the forward line gives the team a focal point and as the game progresses the Scotland players add layer upon layer of confidence to their game. They know that if they get the ball to Law he will make it stick, will make things happen, and, with a minute remaining before half-time, Law clicks onto the ball just outside the penalty area and sends a quick, hard, diagonal pass in behind the Paraguay defence for Graham Leggat, on the right wing, to curl in a cross that Sammy Baird mishits but still gets enough on to jab over the line. Samuel Aguilar, the Paraguay goalkeeper, has sprawled desperately at Baird's feet in an attempt to prevent the goal but he can only push the ball into the inside side netting.

Eight minutes from time, Eligio Echagüe trips Law inside the penalty area as the centre-forward prepares to shoot. Willie Fernie sends Aguilar the wrong way in netting the spot-kick. The Paraguayans, riled at seeing the match slip away from them, start to extract revenge on the Scots, kicking opponents on and off the ball, and when Mackay rips a hairnet from one of their midfield players, holds it triumphantly in the air with one hand and ruffles roughly the player's silken, copious, brown locks, it results in a mass brawl just in front of the section of the ground in which the VIPs are stationed. Shankly, delighted to see his players stick up for one another, cannot disguise a grin as wide as the Idrottsparken's main stand though Willie Allan, next to him, has a face like thunder. The SFA secretary's reaction matters little – Shankly is the boss here and everyone knows it.

The 2–0 win leaves Scotland top of their group. 'We're like one of those collective farms in Russia that you read about,' Shankly tells Tine, the stadium receptionist, after the match. Tine, a slim, bespectacled, middle-aged, elegant blonde, listens politely and attentively, with chin resting on her closed fist, to this lively man from Scotland with the crew cut who is always buzzing with energy and whose desire to engage in friendly conversation with every member of the stadium staff has made him a popular figure with them over the past couple of days, the Scots having used the match venue as their training base prior to the game. Shankly sips from a cup of coffee as he awaits the team getting changed and ready for the coach back to the hotel. Upstairs, a shoal of journalists await the arrival of the Scotland manager in the press room but it is Tine to whom he imparts his post-match analysis.

'It's collective play – we play the ball from the back,' Shankly tells her in his clipped, precise, Ayrshire accent, in which he sounds every vowel and consonant, perfect for imparting rapid bursts of information, delivered staccato-style and with a degree of lyricism unusual in a football manager. 'Improvisation covers the whole affair. It's cat and mouse, it's playing the ball from the back because we realize, me and the players, that you can't score a goal every time you have the ball. How many games end up forty-five goals each?

'You're laughing but, see, it's simple when you think about it. We change shape as the opposition tries to take the ball from us then we hold on to the ball for as long as it takes for an opening to appear and then we sneak a player in, like a thief in the night, and we're quite happy to steal a goal that way. What could be more simple?' Tine smiles empathetically.

'If you can adjust to what happens on the field,' Shankly adds, rattling out his words like gunfire, 'then immediately you've got something. So the players improvise. If they are breaking down one flank and find the way is blocked they switch play to the other flank and work their way ahead from there. These are good, thinking footballers I'm working with here, not any old Tom, Dick or Harry.

'It's designed to be economical and to confuse the opposition. Everyone does their share; it's control and pass, control and pass. If you can control the ball instantly and pass the ball forward quickly it gives you time and the element of surprise. When a player gets the ball we give him two or three options of players to pass it to. With some teams there will be nobody to pass it to – they'll turn their back on you. So for us it's get the ball, give it and then make yourself available for the man on the ball. No long runs – running into no man's land, head down with the ball, oh that's a terrible crime. Instead, pass, give, go and a lot of the time it will look as though you aren't going anywhere but you are constantly pulling and tugging at the opposition's shape so that soon they are looking like a baggy, well-worn jumper, scruffy, ready to be consigned to the dustbin. It's all about improvisation.

'It's like a relay race – no one's asked to do any more than anyone else. They are all sharing, like a collective. Our main aim when we kick off is to give everyone in the team an early touch of the ball. We bring everyone into the game as quickly as possible. If you start off by trying something clever and it breaks down, then it affects the confidence. It's almost scientific; like the team of people that developed the Sputnik. Now wasn't that a quite incredible thing, to do that, send that into space? But you can be sure it wasn't done by one man. Oh no. That would have been a team of people, working day and night to get it right. That's what we're like.'

'Ah, the Russians,' Tine replies, finally finding something in Shankly's words with which she can click. 'So you are like the Russians? You know some people here in Sweden call us the little Russians because everything here is so tightly regulated and the government oversees everything so strictly.'

'Is that so?' Shankly says. 'Tell me, what is it about these swimming baths here in Sweden? I asked for the best place to go for a swim the other day and when I got there it was fellas only and they all were swimming up and down with no clothes on. What's that all about?'

The conversation is about to take an interesting turn – and Shankly is always happy to veer off on to a different topic – when the World Cup press officer reminds him that the journalists have been awaiting his presence for half an hour and are getting restless. Reluctantly, he leaves his coffee and his chat with Tine to join them. The first question comes from a local Swedish reporter.

'Did you think your team was a bit lucky to win today, Mr Shankly?'

The response is short and swift.

'Och away you get, the lot of you.' Shankly says and strolls out of the room.

For all that Scotland have started the tournament well, their third group game will be a risky affair. A draw will be enough to see the Scots through but the French have been in good form, scoring seven against Paraguay and another two against Yugoslavia, albeit in a 3–2 defeat. Just Fontaine, their centre-forward, has already scored five times and on the wing they have Raymond Kopa, who has recently moved to Real Madrid, the European club champions.

The French have to win to go through and if they do so, their hefty goals tally will see them go above the Scots on goal difference, and that would leave Scotland teetering on the brink of elimination and dependent on defeat for Yugoslavia in their match with Paraguay. Despite such a scarifying prospect, Shankly feels, warily, that the team's good start has allowed a degree of complacency to settle upon the squad.

At half past ten on the night before the match with France, a group of players are sitting relaxing on the plush sofas in a corner of the restaurant of their hotel in central Norrköping, in which, as Shankly has observed, some players have been making the most of the cooked breakfasts and the three-course meals available both for lunch and dinner. The hospitality at suppertime is also lavish and while sandwiches and tea are the choice for most of the Scottish players, Tommy Younger, the goalkeeper, has opted for a large slice of creamy Swedish cake and now returns to the counter to take another piece. Doug Cowie is serenading the players with a tune on his guitar when Younger, habitually the life and soul of the party, settles down beside the other players and is silent for once as he happily digs into the rich concoction, giving it all his concentration. Shankly suddenly appears from behind a pillar and takes a seat opposite Younger, watching him intently. As Younger lifts his fork for a third mouthful, Shankly casually asks him, 'That your first slice of cake, Tommy?' The goal-keeper hesitates slightly, then replies, 'Eh, yes, boss.'

Shankly looks over at the pristine, refrigerated cake compartment, filled with all varieties of delicacies. 'Good,' the manager says, 'Good, because, you know, boys, moderation is a very important thing. Everything in moderation is good for you: a piece of steak, a drink of beer, cake . . . in fact, seeing you there, Tommy, enjoying that cake so much, I think I'll order a slice. Jackie, would you go and bring me a slice of that big meringue cake – that one with the strawberries and oranges and cream?'

The cake duly having been brought over to Shankly by Jackie Mudie, the forward, the manager looks at it, scruti-nizing it and noting the lavish cream filling. 'My, that looks appetizing, doesn't it boys? You wouldn't expect cakes like that in Sweden, would you? How many of us thought that when we got here there would be stuff like that available for us? Correct me if I'm wrong but Sweden isn't renowned for cake-baking and making, is it?'

Younger, a large, heavily built lad, with a goofy smile, is quick to agree that the quality of cake has been an agreeable surprise.

'I can see you enjoyed that, Tommy,' Shankly says as the goalkeeper finishes off his portion. 'So, here, have this piece too. It's only your second of the night. Go on.'

The goalkeeper hesitates and declines.

'No no, Tommy, I insist,' Shankly says, holding up his arms in mock protest. 'I got it especially for you.'

Younger allows himself to be persuaded but, now on his

third slice of cake, finds it harder to dig his way through the rich, sugary product. A waitress arrives to remove the plate from his previous piece and Shankly asks her to bring another slice of cake to the table, which is now in near silence as Mudie, Eddie Turnbull, Tommy Docherty, John Hewie and Doug Cowie watch Younger make slow progress through his third slice.

'Can you bring over a piece of that chocolate one? And make it a large slice,' Shankly says to the waitress, pointing at a torte decorated with chocolate buttons. Younger pauses, fork hanging in the air. 'Go on, Tommy,' Shankly exhorts, 'get wired in.'

When, finally, Younger finishes the meringue, Shankly slides the plate with the chocolate cake across to him. 'On you go, Tommy,' Shankly says, 'fill your boots.' 'No, no, boss, I couldn't,' Younger says. 'I think I'd be sick.' Shankly nods. 'You're quite right, lad. Moderation in all things.' Younger looks relieved. 'Now,' Shankly tells him, instantaneously, 'go and ask Dawson Walker to kit you out in your tracksuit and bring your boots and meet me in the lobby in ten minutes.'

Having ordered a taxi to the Idrottsparken, Shankly, armed with a bag of footballs, arrives at the ground with an apprehensive Younger and persuades the night watchman, another stadium operative whom he has made a point of getting to know, to switch on the floodlights for him. Shankly, in brogues, raincoat, collar and tie, then puts the goalkeeper through an intense training session, firing ball after ball at him for forty-five minutes, during which Younger is violently and colourfully sick behind the goal, twice.

'Well done, lad, well done,' Shankly says, as they wind up. 'Goodness me, it's two minutes to twelve. We'll call it a day there. Moderation in all things.'

The Scots have several injury concerns prior to the match with France. Mudie's mobility in training has been hampered by an injury sustained in the match with Paraguay, during which he was kicked in the back when lying on the ground after making a tackle. Graham Leggat has sustained a wrist injury in a tussle with the Paraguayan goalkeeper. John Hewie and Jimmy Murray have been struggling with injuries received in the game against the Yugoslavs, while Bobby Evans has a groin strain.

It means that Scotland delay naming their team until the morning of the match with the French but when they do, the biggest surprise is the omission of Younger, a fixture in the side who has made twenty-four appearances, in an un-broken run, during the previous three years. His replacement is to be Bill Brown, who is making his debut in this vital encounter. Following Shankly's announcement of the team, in a side room in their hotel, Younger encounters the manager in a corridor and asks, 'Why have you left me out of the team, boss?' Shankly ignores him completely, does not even look in his direction, and proceeds on his way.

'I never discuss the opposition, never,' Shankly is telling Torbjorn, the team's coach driver, shortly before the Scotland party are to depart the Grand Hotel for their game with the French in Örebro. 'One of the players came out of the tactical talk before this match and said, "Are Kopa and Fontaine not playing?" Now that was music to my ears.' Torbjorn nods, with a huge smile that he hopes does not betray the fact that his English is extremely limited and that he has no idea what this man is telling him. 'You see, Torbjorn, we don't frighten ourselves by talking about how great the opposition are. We only concern ourselves with what we do.

'Ninety minutes is a long time to be worrying about the opposition, isn't it? Instead, I make a joke in the team talk. I said to them, "France reckon they play champagne football" – and they do, it's true. I heard that Kopa said that very thing because he and several others of the France team are from Reims, where they make the champagne. So I said to my players, "After they've played you, they'll feel as though they've had a dozen pints of heavy on an empty stomach. They will be reeling." Eh? Ha ha.

'So you see, Torbjorn, this lightens up the atmosphere and also reduces the opposition to human proportions.' The bulky coach driver smiles broadly again, offers Shankly a bonbon and stretches both arms in the air.

· 1958 · 1958 · 1958 · 1958 · 1958 · 1958 · 1958 · 1958 · 1958 · 1958 ·

There are 13,500 spectators, including a smattering of Scots, inside the Eyravallen Stadium, Örebro, as the Scots and the French trot on to the park. With only two minutes gone, Jean Vincent, France's sleek outside-right, darts into the penalty area with the ball and lets fly with a powerful shot that is heading for the roof of the net until Brown leaps to fist it over the crossbar. That is the clearest opening of the early stages but Scotland soon begin to assert themselves more and more forcefully.

Bobby Collins, a winger at club level, has been given a different role by Shankly, operating in a central area behind four forwards – and the French cannot pin him down. After twenty-one minutes he careers forward and pings a pass into the heart of the French penalty area, where all Murray has to do is sidefoot the ball neatly past Claude Abbes, the France goalkeeper. Shortly before full-time, Baird cracks the ball past Abbes to make it 2–0 and Raymond Kaelbel, the France defender, in frustration, smacks the celebrating Collins on the mouth. The 'Wee Barra' responds with a flurry of punches and soon there is an all-out brawl taking place. Juan Brazzi, the Argentinian referee, and his linesmen break it up and Brazzi calls the two team captains together and instructs them to tell their players to calm down. This duly done, only a couple of minutes remain before he sounds the final whistle and hand-shakes are exchanged warmly all round.

This time Shankly strides into the press room a mere five minutes after the conclusion of the match, taking by surprise the assembled members of the fourth estate who, expecting another extended wait for the manager, are starting to pass the time by snacking on delicious, fresh, open sandwiches. They hurriedly put down their snacks and coffees and gather around Shankly.

'We've just beaten the team regarded as the best in this competition,' Shankly tells the press before any of them can ask an opening question. 'What a player that Kopa is! He can play – twisty and turny – but maybe a bit flash? You know, in qualifying for this competition, we defeated Spain, knocked them out of the World Cup before they could even get to the finals of a tournament they were expected to win – that was

Di Stéfano, Kubala, Suárez and all them. They told us before we played them that they were the best team in the world. Yes, sir. This Scotland team played West Germany, the world champions, in front of 80,000 in Stuttgart last year, and beat them 3–1. We played Poland in Warsaw in front of 70,000, shortly before we came here, beat them, and the Poles said it was the best display they had seen from any team since the war. These are unembroidered facts. I am not elaborating on the truth in any way.

'So we must be taken seriously in this competition. We were told that the Spanish were a team of supermen, same with the French, but I said to the boys that they are just eleven men in jerseys. Scotland can win this World Cup but I can see that you all still don't believe me. Well, let me ask you this. A year ago, would you have believed that it would be possible to put a dog in space? Would you have believed that Laika the dog would have been launched in a specially fitted rocket and survived happily? When you think about it like that, Scotland winning the World Cup doesn't seem so impossible, does it? That's all.' With that Shankly strides out of the room, two minutes after his entrance, leaving a gaggle of habitually garrulous press men standing agog and in silence.

· 1958 · 1958 · 1958 · 1958 · 1958 · 1958 · 1958 · 1958 · 1958 · 1958 ·

An exhilarating touch of finesse settles the Scots' quarter-final with Northern Ireland, again in Norrköping's Idrottsparken, fast becoming something akin to a home ground for the Scots. A dour duel has reached the forty-fourth minute when Danny Blanchflower, the most artistically inclined player in the Irish team, advances down the left wing in his habitual, unhurried fashion before attempting yet another delicate-as-a-fairycake flick with his right boot but as he goes to make the pass he loses his balance slightly and Bobby Collins seizes the opportunity to take the ball. He powers forward with it across the halfway line, well aware that the Irish, committed to going forward, are now short of men at the back. Collins shuttles the ball forward to Mudie, who whips it on again to Law, bursting through the middle and, played onside by Alf McMichael, the Northern Ireland left-back, Law is now one on one with Harry Gregg, the goalkeeper, who stands up tall, but as Law powers down on him he fairly bludgeons the ball under the goalkeeper's body and into the net.

After the interval, Scotland dominate. Law heads in Baird's cross ten minutes into the second period, then nicks a lob over Gregg for his hat trick. A late counter from Baird makes it 4–0 and the Scots are in the semi-finals.

'Once Law is through with only the goalkeeper to beat,' Shankly tells Nils, the hotel gardener, back at the Grand Hotel, 'when you see Law through on a goalkeeper like that, you can get your tea out and drink it. You know it's going to be a goal. If the goalie stays on the line he will run up to him and put it past him. If he comes up to Law, he'll go round him and put it in from a bad angle.

'You know, Law wouldn't be here if it wasn't for me. He plays for me at Huddersfield, did you know that? Yes, he does and I had to persuade very gently the committee members of our football association that it was worthwhile bringing along this eighteen-year-old boy who had never played for his country before this World Cup. They agreed, reluctantly. "On your head be it," they said. Can you believe it? In other words, they'll be happy to take the credit if the boy does well but the blame will be laid firmly at my door if it proves too much for him. See, there's always a lot of politics in football but you've just got to deal with it.

'Anyway, I've tried to nurture the lad carefully since he came down to us from Aberdeen; just in the very same way as you nurture these roses, eh? You tend them, care for them gently, monitor their progress, give them the right conditions to grow? Am I right? You know, my brother John went to a team when he was a boy and they ended up making him overstrain a heart muscle. That was so sad for him but you learn lessons from that and it taught me to go easy on young boys, not to overtrain them, and that's what I've done with Law. He had special training, sometimes on his own, or sometimes with just two or three a side, sessions that he liked and we gradually built him up with food like steak and drinks such as milk – he was like a stick when he came to us – and it has worked. By going gently on him it means that on the day of a match he gives you everything. He wouldn't be able to do that at his size and weight if he had been trained hard, trained to excess. That's a good-looking flower there – what's that one called?'

· 1958 · 1958 · 1958 · 1958 · 1958 · 1958 · 1958 · 1958 · 1958 · 1958 ·

It is a contented Dawson Walker, happy to be in Sweden in his familiar role as trainer, alongside whom Shankly settles on a bench in the hotel grounds two days later. Walker has been breathing an extended sigh of relief ever since the SFA informed him that he would be going to Sweden in his usual capacity and not, as they had originally mooted, as team manager. Watching Shankly go about his business in expert fashion has only emphasized to the Clyde man just how lucky he has been in being excused that duty by the SFA and that relief has added an extra zest to the way he has gone about his work, making him unflickeringly supportive and helpful to Shankly.

'You know, Dawson,' Shankly says, in a rare contemplative tone, 'there are a lot of teams that don't know what they're trying to do. They mystify me – and not in a good way. That's why I would buy this entire Scotland team for Huddersfield Town if I had the money because I know it would be a sound investment. All these players need is handling – not being bullied or pushed around. When we Scots are all working together we'll take a bit of beating. It would be criminal for a Scottish team not to be successful given the players we've got.

'We don't need to motivate these players because they're winners – I've told them that repeatedly – so there's no need to gee them up. Tommy Docherty, for one, is the same type of player as me, a right-half. I said to Tommy, "Just put my jersey on, Tom, and it'll guide you round." That's what he did and that's what happened; he's wearing my Scotland jersey! He's a good player and a hard man and I love having him in my team. I'm loath, though, to put one player in front of another. I work for them and they work for me.

'Now, even when you believe in your own players and even when you know how good they are, there are some times when you have to accept that there are other teams that might just be that bit better than you. I'm beginning to think that could be the case when we play Brazil. You know, Dawson, all of Brazil's matches have taken place at the same time as ours so I've not been able to watch them play but I do know all about them.'

'How have you managed that, boss?' Walker asks, puzzled.

'Well, Dawson,' Shankly says, ' I asked a very good friend of mine to watch other teams playing; a man I can trust very well, a man I've worked with before, and this is where you come in.'

'Is it?' Walker says.

'Yes,' Shankly replies. 'You see, the man in question is Andy Beattie, the man who got me the job at Huddersfield, and you know and I know that he is not too popular with the SFA after the last World Cup – when he rubbed a few of the committee men up the wrong way and was then eased out of the manager's job. Now I called him out to Sweden to do a bit of work for me and he has seen three of Brazil's games so he knows every one of their players, players like this Didi and Dida and Vava and Pelé; my goodness even their names make me dizzy, their names are like magical, musical notes. So, I need Andy on the bench beside me for this semi-final, to help guide me through it the way we worked at Huddersfield when he was manager and I was his assistant – that was before he decided to get out of it all and run his post office in Preston – and this, as I say, is where you come in. I want you to put Andy in the hamper.'

'In the hamper?'

'That's right,' Shankly says. 'When we arrive on the coach for the match, Andy will be in there, in beside the kit. You'll keep it a secret, even from the boys, and ten minutes before the game begins, when we know that all the SFA people are up in the directors' lounge feeding their faces, you'll bring him out and he can then sit beside me on the bench. By the time anyone catches on, it'll be too late for them to do anything about it.'

· 1958 · 1958 · 1958 · 1958 · 1958 · 1958 · 1958 · 1958 · 1958 · 1958 ·

Ten minutes before kick-off against Brazil, Shankly is readying his team, a set of players still startled at Beattie bouncing out of the hamper and swiftly reacquainting himself with those who were with him at the last World Cup. It has given the players a lift and the distraction of it all has displaced any apprehension about facing Brazil, whose reputation has grown fearsomely during this World Cup. Shankly, watched by a grinning Beattie, is now roving around the room, doling out last-minute words of advice; chit-chat intended as balm to soothe the players' minds before the rough and tumble of battle.

'I want you to speak to each other with the ball; I want to see fluent conversationalists, practised speakers, individuals well versed in the language of the game. I go to see games and I see teams whose players look as though they've never been introduced, so when they try to speak to each other with the ball there are misunderstandings, misapprehensions – it is as if they are using different languages sometimes. I don't want to see any of that out there today.

'Don't argue with the referee – you're not going to change his mind. My brother Alec told me about that. I've had goals disallowed against me and some people in my team are going frantic – this is as a player – going mad but not me, oh no . . . and I'm not the most patient of people, I'll tell you that now. I'm what you call an impatient patient man. So I'd say,

"Okay, referee you're right, good decision." It meant I maybe got away with a little bit that others didn't.

'So, Tommy Docherty, I want you to be the referee's friend on the pitch. If there's a little break in the play, Tom, go up to the referee and say, "That was a good decision, there," even if it has gone against one of our players. Next time the referee has to make a decision he might just give it in your favour. I want you to converse with the referee – flannel him. The trouble with referees is that they know the rules but they don't know the game so you have to convince them that you are on their side – that you think they're doing a great job – and they will like you for that. This is brains—'

For all that Shankly's bright words have buoyed up the players and taken their minds off the daunting prospect of facing the Brazilians, it takes only two minutes for the Brazilians to undo the Scots; Vava, the centre-forward, clipping a low shot past Brown. With Beattie on the bench pinpointing the strengths and weaknesses in the opposition, Shankly adjusts his team and the Scots start to probe at the Brazilian defence like a dentist poking around to try to discover hidden cavities in a patient's gleaming teeth. After nine minutes Murray sends Law streaking free, in behind a back line that has pushed up high. Shankly, unselfconsciously and unaware that he is doing so, mimes pouring a cup of tea from a teapot and, sure enough, Law rounds Gylmar dos Santos, the Brazil goalkeeper, and ekes out a low shot that rolls between the scrambling Brazilian and his left-hand post.

The contest remains an even one until midway through the half, when Vava crunches into a challenge on Bobby Evans, slamming his right forearm heavily into the centre-half's jaw and using his right boot to stamp on the Scot's leg. It leaves Evans limping heavily and two minutes later, Didi is unattended when he slips a low shot past Brown. The Scots retreat into defence to cover for their injured captain and Shankly curses SFA intransigence; prior to the tournament Allan and his fellow SFA officials, plus those of the Football Association, had threatened that Scotland and England would scratch from the World Cup if a FIFA motion to allow substitutes were to be upheld.

At the interval a pain-killing injection is administered to Evans, enabling him to walk around delicately but to do little more. It will emerge after the match that the Scottish captain has been playing with a broken tibia. With Evans debilitated, and effectively a passenger, Scotland lose two further goals before Baird's late strike adds a gloss of respectability to the final score of 4–2 in Brazil's favour.

'He's a light heavyweight, he runs like a gazelle,' Shankly says over his shoulder, still walking, in answer to a question about Pelé from a pressman waiting for him outside the ground. Defeat is the only entity that can stop, temporarily, the flow of words from this most garrulous of individuals. At home, he responds to a setback for Huddersfield by remaining in his house after the match and scrubbing clean every corner of his kitchen. That's why, later on the evening of the match with Brazil, the Scotland manager can be found, apron around his waist, scrubbing down the surfaces of the Grand Hotel's kitchen and starting to find his voice again in breezy conversation with the hotel's chef and waiters. Three days later, confidence regained, he sends out a team that defeats West Germany 3–2 in Gothenburg to clinch third place in the tournament. For Shankly, it is still a frustrating experience: winning a match but not being able to build on it; for him, third in the World Cup is as good, or bad, as finishing sixteenth. Later that evening, he can be found in the Swedish port's dockland, almost manic at the controls of a crane, having persuaded its operator to let him have a shot at some derelict buildings with a wrecking-ball.

· 1958 · 1958 · 1958 · 1958 · 1958 · 1958 · 1958 · 1958 · 1958 · 1958 ·

At home, third place is received as a triumph even though those among the Scottish population lucky enough to have televisions have seen only glimpses of their team in the tournament, thanks to erratic programming courtesy of the Eurovision link. Some Scots are of the belief that with young players such as Law, Brown and Mackay, the national team can now go on to even greater things; others think that, like Sputnik, Scotland's 1950s glory on the world stage has been brief, bright but unrepeatable.

A MATCH FOR A MAVERICK?

A bullet zings into the wall of Viña del Mar's Hotel Marrissa and only narrowly misses the slim figure of a man, clad in sombrero and poncho. Weaving and winding, he rounds a corner and leaps on to the bonnet and then the roof of a car, which allows him to scramble on to the top of the wall just as another bullet whistles over his head. He tumbles down into the hotel grounds and uses the inside of the wall for cover as he sprints for a clump of trees. His pursuers are now scaling the wall but four armed security guards, roused – two from deep slumber, two from a card game – by the noise are scurrying toward the source of the disturbance. *'Vamos!'* shouts one of the chasing gunmen on sight of the guards, and he and his *compadres* abandon the chase, yelling angry imprecations over the wall as they retreat.

Having discarded his South American 'couture' behind some bushes near the hotel entrance, Jim Baxter, the Scotland midfield player, strolls into the vestibule of the hotel, deserted at three o'clock in the morning, and, with a broad, silly grin all over his face, ascends the stairs to his room as quietly as he can.

Fortunately, the recent commotion in the grounds has disturbed none of the hotel's sleeping guests, with the Scottish Football Association officials among those in deepest slumber after another good evening's hospitality in downtown Viña del Mar, the beautiful Chilean seaside resort that is the base for Scotland's tilt at the 1962 World Cup.

One guest, though, is very much awake, and once Baxter has safely entered the premises a third-floor window from which Matt Busby, the manager, has listened to and observed much of the action unfolding below, is gently closed. In a nearby street, a taxi driver happily motors off with the largest tip he has ever received – even in this pleasant, weekend seaside retreat for Chile's rich – and pesos spill from the man's pockets as his reward for hightailing it across town at Baxter's request. Less happy is the father of a local girl, who, together with his three sons, had been pursuing a gringo decked out in a parody of South American costume, whom he had found enjoying a horizontal version of the twist with his only daughter on the resort's otherwise lifeless beach in the early hours of this morning.

· 1962 · 1962 · 1962 · 1962 · 1962 · 1962 · 1962 · 1962 · 1962 · 1962 ·

At breakfast, there is no sign of Baxter, and with players starting to return to their rooms to prepare for the morning's training session, Willie Allan, the SFA secretary, sitting at the same table as Busby, wonders aloud why the ebullient Fifer has absented himself from the morning repast.

'I told him he could remain in bed for a bit longer this morning,' Busby tells Allan, calmly. 'He got quite a tough time of it yesterday against Spain from some of their defenders, as you know, so I think a bit of extra rest will do him the world of good.'

Allan concurs but in subdued fashion, not entirely convinced that one player, no matter how extraordinarily good, should be given special favours. Unwilling to disagree with Busby, though, he opts not to express his opinion, not least because Baxter is the man who supplied the peerless pass from which Willie Henderson, the eighteen-year-old winger, scored the only goal in the Scots' opening match the day before – and against a star-spangled Spanish side.

When Baxter does finally surface, at lunchtime, the hotel is quiet. His squad-mates and Busby are out, varying their training by having a bounce game on the beach with waiters from the hotel, the type of gentle workout suitable for the day after a demanding match. Busby says nothing to Baxter when the party returns to the hotel nor does he confront the player at any time prior to the next game, against Mexico, three days later. He does not even say anything after a 3–1 defeat to the Mexicans that leaves Scotland's progress in the competition hanging by a thread.

It is the first game, in thirteen attempts, that the Mexicans have won in the World Cup finals and they beat the Scots despite conceding, unluckily, a first-minute goal when John White hits his shot down into the turf, whence it bounces up and over the grounded Antonio Carbajal, the Mexico goal-keeper. Mexico hit back with three goals that all come from ventures down their right flank where Baxter, the Scotland left-half, has been exposed through pushing far forward frequently and not bothering to cover for his team-mates when the Mexicans are attacking. It leaves Eric Caldow, the left-back, stretched in doing the work of two men and too exposed to prevent the darting, rapier-like thrusts of the cavalier Mexicans.

Some players are desperate for Busby to admonish Baxter but, after the Mexico debacle – and with the third and vital group game, against Brazil, coming up in four days' time – Busby, instead, addresses the players as a whole. 'That wasn't very good,' he says, in typically understated fashion of the performance against the Mexicans. 'I will always back you when you are building up play, building up, being construc-tive, but that didn't happen today. So what I'll say to you lads is that, this being the night after a game, you are free to do whatever you wish this evening. Do whatever you think fit after that performance.'

Several of the players get their manager's message and confine themselves to the hotel, sinking a slow beer or two and playing cards, others stroll downtown to a gaudy café and, over delicious coffee and ice creams, discuss how the game went so wrong for Scotland. Baxter, in contrast, ropes a couple of the younger squad players into hitting nearby Valparaiso for the night.

The following morning, en route to training, one result of his carousing becomes substantially evident when he vomits all over the back seat of the team coach, leading to much loud protest on the part of his team-mates. Baxter, white as a sheet, then slumps across a double seat and goes to sleep until, after being roused at the training venue, he drowsily stumbles, shuffles and groans through the morning's exer-cises. After a time, when he thinks the manager is not looking,

Baxter slips off to hide on the coach where he soon falls into a deep slumber from which he awakes only when the vehicle draws up outside their hotel. Again, Busby has noted everything but says nothing.

Baxter is restored to rude self-confidence by the day of the match with Brazil, which will take place at the modest little stadium in Vina del Mar, where crowds barely into five figures have watched the games in group three. With three-quarters of an hour remaining before the game begins he sits in a corner of the dressing room, ready for action in Scotland shirt, socks and shorts, his legs crossed, body slouched against the wall and a lit cigarette between his fingers.

'See this ground,' Baxter opines loudly, 'it's more fit for a village fair than for a World Cup. Still, it makes it easier to get a good eyeful of the local birds, eh? You should have seen the one I had last night at that El Niño Loco. Hey, I'll tell you what – she had no need for a girdle . . .' At that moment, Busby walks into the dressing room to read out the team and chooses to ignore the star player's boasts. The manager has left the announcement of the line-up until this late stage because, he says, he had wished to see who the Brazilians will be fielding: 'Brown, Hamilton, Caldow,' Busby reads in his calm, mellow voice, 'Crerand, McNeill, Mackay, Smith, White, St John, Law and Wilson.'

Baxter throws down his smoke and is ready to launch into a tirade against Busby but the manager simply walks out of the room without another word. The player goes to follow Busby and give him an earful for omitting him from the team but is restrained by his team-mates and, persuaded by them of the folly of pursuing Busby, he, instead, throws off his kit, and, dressing in a rage, makes a swift exit from the stadium, commanding a taxi driver to take him to the nearest bar.

Scotland, with the hard-working Mackay in Baxter's place, earn a dogged 0–0 draw with the world champions. It still leaves the Scots sweating on their progress and the following day the Scottish party, minus Baxter, still AWOL, troop along to the stadium to watch the Mexicans face Spain. Mexico need only draw to pip the Scots to second place in the group. It is a long afternoon for the Scots although Busby remains a picture of calm as they watch a Mexican side, set up to defend, repel numerous goal attempts from the Spaniards. Carbajal is in defiant form, but one minute from time the goalkeeper makes his first slip of the day when he fails to hold a shot from Paco Gento, the winger, and Joaquín Peiró nips the rebound into the net, leaving Carbajal – a fixture in the Mexico team for the past four World Cups and playing in what he says is his final tournament – sprawled on the turf and in tears. The goalkeeper's moment of misery is, for the Scots, one of exultation – they are in the quarter-finals.

Later that afternoon, as the last of the day's sunshine dapples the whitewashed walls around the Hotel Marrissa's swimming pool, Willie Allan, wearing full SFA regalia, is relaxing in a poolside deckchair. The SFA secretary is dipping his toes in the water and contemplating a sip of his Scotch and soda when Baxter, finally returning to the hotel, quietly walks up from behind and tips Allan into the water – whisky tumbler, spectacles, braces and all. It is an act of rebellion against a staid figure of authority, carried out by a player described by teammates as a 'headbanger'. Baxter scurries away undetected while Allan, a non-swimmer, is rescued by a pool lifeguard, attracted to the near-deserted swimming zone by Allan's screams of panic. Restored to dry land, the spluttering secretary vows revenge on his assailant but, for all his suspicions, Allan cannot be certain as to the perpetrator of this terrible act.

· 1962 · 1962 · 1962 · 1962 · 1962 · 1962 · 1962 · 1962 · 1962 · 1962 ·

There is no further sign of Baxter and later that evening when there is still no indication of the player's return, Busby decides to visit the room that Baxter shares with Pat Crerand. He waits until Crerand is settled safely downstairs in the lounge, relaxing with some team-mates, then goes to take a look. Baxter's section of the room is chaotic, with clothes and training gear scattered around willy-nilly, but prominent among the player's possessions Busby finds a piece of paper that has been glued on to cardboard backing, the paper featuring some words, and immediately Busby wonders whether it might be a prayer or a poem to help an individual, far from home, through testing times. Busby picks it up and reads:

```
Pause for. Cooling of fevered high-brow. Grab the
glasses. Out with the ice. In with the Cossack.
And soda. Or could be squash. Tomato juice. Bubbly
cordial or still cool water. 'Cos everything goes
with Cossack Vodka. Including inspiration. And so
on to a happy ending. Set sail, captain.'
```

The Scotland manager reads the text – clearly cut from a newspaper advertisement – for a second time, then sets it down, takes another look around the room and pads softly out.

These are not easy days for Busby. His Manchester United team have failed to spring back from the Munich Disaster of

1958 and the tragedy that beset the Busby Babes is looking to have become an irrecoverable blow. The Old Trafford side's form has been indifferent for four consecutive seasons, with the prospect even of relegation on the horizon in the most recent, 1961–2, season. There remains sympathy and affection for Busby in Manchester but, even so, rumours are growing that his position as United's manager may be in jeopardy. He has aged rapidly since Munich but when the SFA offered him this World Cup opportunity he was unable to resist. The change of scenery, competition and players, he feels, will be as good as a holiday and will refresh his senses but he is aware that Scotland's indifferent start to the World Cup may confirm to some back home that he has lost his touch.

Baxter appears to be the antithesis of Busby. The latter is a softly spoken, avuncular, quiet and thoughtful individual now well set in middle age, a stage of life that seems to suit perfectly his unrushed, considered, careful personality: his bulky form, rapidly balding head and habitual pipe-smoking complete the safe, secure image. Baxter, in contrast, is a loud-mouth, recklessly disrespectful of authority and, complete with a bushy thatch of tousled hair, an embodiment of the new wave of British youth whose rebellious attitude to life is causing so many social commentators to express concern about the way society is developing. There's a new music culture where pop and jazz stars cause riotous frenzy in concert halls and spark mass hysteria among their young followers, many of whom are characterized as work shy by their elders – and whose casually hedonistic approach is epitomized by adver-tisements such as the one that Baxter clearly finds so appealing.

It is all part of a new world reflected in images of glam-orous, skimpily clad, 'available' young women and sharply dressed, arrogant young men. The young have more money in their pockets than Busby's generation ever did, and this new world is alien to the former miner from Lanarkshire who, as a small boy, lost his father in the First World War and who consequently, through becoming the replacement head of his household in his mid-teens, had regularity, reliability and responsibility thrust upon him from his early youth.

At half past six the following morning, Busby, wrapped in a bulky coat against the chill of a South American winter dawn, strolls out of the hotel grounds and soon hits his steady stride on the pink-paved walkway that leads to the harbour of this town with its bright, pastel-coloured houses. He is soon making his way along the beach and puffing on his first pipe of the day. After ten minutes he finds what he has been seeking: Baxter, fast asleep under the hull of a rowing boat. Busby does not shake him awake but, more subtly, he coughs twice – though without garnering any reaction from Baxter. A few more coughs from the older man and Baxter stirs, finally, opening a pair of dazed eyes and taking in the sight of the long, flat beach and Busby standing before him.

'Hello Jim,' Busby says. 'How are you this morning?' His tone is as friendly and casual as if he is greeting Baxter on arrival in the breakfast room at the hotel. The player is too stiff, surprised and hung-over to respond. 'Well, that was a bit of a kerfuffle at the Brazil game, wasn't it?' Busby continues. 'I didn't see you after I read out the team – and you weren't about when we came back in from the match. Someone suggested to me that you had left the stadium but I know that you would have followed the SFA rule that players must remain and watch the match, even if not in the team or on the substitutes' bench. Anyway, I was far too busy with the match once it had started to have a look for you – and then, later on, you were nowhere to be seen but I understand you probably wanted a little bit of time to yourself.

'So, having a fair idea that a Fife lad might fancy a sleep on the beach, I brought you your breakfast.' From behind his back, Busby produces a bottle of vodka, inducing an immediate reaction from Baxter, who stumbles to his feet and, clinging on to the boat with his left hand, steps away a couple of yards and is violently sick on the sand. Busby says nothing, waiting for the player to right himself. Baxter, in creased SFA blazer and with one shoe missing, stumbles to the shore and douses his face in Pacific sea water before returning, sheepishly, to his manager. 'You'll be feeling healthier after that,' the older man says. 'Jim,' he adds, 'is this how you want to live your life? I'm not saying it's wrong but is this what you want for yourself; drinking yourself to oblivion, clinging to a bottle for comfort?

'It's up to you but if it is, I doubt you'll see too many more World Cups. You know, I shouldn't really tell you this – I'm not supposed to discuss club business while I'm with the international team – but Real Madrid are interested in you. Half the Spain team are from Real and the Real manager watched them play against us. They liked what they saw of you. Nothing may come of it this time but that shows you where you can go in your career. Now it's not for me to come along here like some sort of headmaster and lay down the law to you – I know that you are an independent man, with your own ideas and your own life to lead in your own style, and I know that you will make your own decision on how to go about all that.'

Baxter remains silent and, propped against the rowing boat, looks away across the bay. For all the player's bluster, Busby has correctly deduced that Baxter is, at heart, a shy individual whose loud persona is something of a shield to combat the stresses involved in his having moved from rural Fife and the fun of a game with Raith Rovers, to big-city life in Glasgow and the sharp scrutiny involved in playing for Rangers – with the accompanying adulation from thousands of intense supporters and the contrasting loneliness of living in an unfamiliar city

'You know, Jim, the best way you can show the world your individuality,' Busby goes on, 'is to do what you can do on the football field. You are a special type of player. Of course, there are players on the same level as you but they have different qualities, a different style, a different way of playing the game: you are unique.

'Drinking a bottle of vodka? Anyone can do that. You know, when I was a young man, I smoked a pipe, as I still do, and there was a lot of talk about that. You wouldn't believe it, would you, that that could be an issue? No one remembers that now, no one comes up and talks to me about how I smoked a pipe as a young man but they do come up to me and tell me that they remember me as a player. I'm sure that when you reflect upon it, you will want the same for yourself.'

The Scotland manager carefully places the bottle in the base of the rowing boat, a present for some unsuspecting local, and puts his arm around Baxter. 'Now, let's find somewhere that will give us a decent breakfast.'

· 1962 · 1962 · 1962 · 1962 · 1962 · 1962 · 1962 · 1962 · 1962 · 1962 ·

'Yes, this is the best Scotland side I have seen,' Lajos Baróti, the Hungary manager, tells his own country's press in advance of his team's quarter-final with Busby's side. 'I saw their first two matches, against Mexico and Spain, but I have to say that they still don't learn. They still play everything the same way – through the number six. Hold him and you've held Scotland. If we do that, they will have nobody else to dictate the game.'

When a Scottish reporter relays Baróti's comments to Busby, the manager asks, 'Is that right? Is that what he really said?' Busby is sitting in the television lounge of the hotel with the squad, watching a replay of Hungary's previous match. The black and white picture is rather grainy and on the small screen it is close to impossible to tell which player is which. These television pictures cannot be used as a guide for his players to get to know properly the facial and physical features of opponents; it is only on the field when, face to face, live and in colour, the players can identify, on the day, their opponents individually. An idea flashes through Busby's mind and a smile plays on his lips.

· 1962 · 1962 · 1962 · 1962 · 1962 · 1962 · 1962 · 1962 · 1962 · 1962 ·

Kick-off against the Hungarians is approaching and Busby's team are preparing to head out for their usual five-minute, pre-match warm-up when the manager puts his idea into practice: Baxter, who has become identified iconically as Scotland's number six, is instead handed a number three shirt; Denis Law receives a number seven; Willie Henderson, the diminutive winger, a number four, and so on, until every member of the team, other than Bill Brown, the goalkeeper, is taking the field with a number alien to him and to the position he plays on the field.

Baxter's number six shirt has been given to Alex Hamilton,

the right-back, and it is only when the match begins that confusion is sparked on the touchline and the Hungarian right-half can be seen wandering around in a state of confusion because the Scottish number six, whom he has been detailed to man-mark and whom he can identify only by his numbered shirt, is deep in defence on the right rather than on the left in the middle of the park, where he had expected him to be. The Hungarian dutifully sticks to Baróti's specific instructions and marks tightly his opponent – albeit with a look of serious puzzlement all over his face.

The Hungarians are still trying to get to grips with the jumbled numbers, cleverly set out to sow maximum confusion in their ranks, when a Scots attack opens the scoring, after only four minutes. For all that these are two good ball-playing sides, the goal is deceptively simple. Bill Brown's long kick from hands deep into the Hungarian half takes one bounce and Ian St John sweeps on to the ball and cracks a low shot under the falling body of Gyula Grosics, the Hungary goalkeeper. It proves to be the only counter in what settles down to become a closely fought match. Busby's trick with the shirts was always going to have a short-lived effect but the Scots have capitalized on the brief confusion before the Hungarians start concentrating on picking up players by where they are operating on the field.

Baxter's performance is world-class, the player pinging balls around freely. Busby has given him the option to move wherever he wishes on the field, with the more disciplined Dave Mackay filling in for Baxter either whenever a defensive gap needs to be plugged or joining the attack when Baxter is absent and numbers are short. It is still the more flamboyant man who receives the praise of the press after the Scots have seen out a 1–0 victory.

Reporting from Chile, Hughie 'the Voice of Scottish Football' Andrews writes of Baxer:

> He's the swashbuckling cavalier of Scottish soccer,
> the golden boy of Ibrox on whom the football sun
> always seems to shine. The golden boy with the
> '60s style and the jersey hanging outside his
> pants that makes soccer stylists wince – he lets
> Scotland switch from power to precision. A glit-
> tering curtain of praise from foreigners at this
> World Cup hangs around him like the cloak of a
> noble; or, better still, the robe of a sun king.

More earthy concerns are on the minds of Baxter's fellow Scots as they prepare to meet another communist nation, Yugoslavia, in the semi-finals. A win will bring each player a bonus of £400, a sum equivalent to a month's wages at a top British club and, for those Scots playing for the more modest clubs in their native league, half a year's pay. It means that money is on their minds as they sit around the swimming pool at the Hotel Marrissa the day after the Hungary game.

'I'll be getting a Lanco Swiss watch,' 'Hammy' Hamilton, the Dundee player, asserts confidently, running his hand over his crew-cut and grinning widely. 'It costs twelve guineas – saw it in the paper.'

Bill Brown chimes in, 'I've had the wife on the phone and we've settled on a Rolls Rapide.'

Billy McNeill looks over at him, 'What's that? A variation on the Rolls-Royce?'

Brown laughs, 'No, it's a washing machine but one with a difference – it's got variable fabric control with swirl and jet action. Its name is no mistake, it is the sleekest washing machine on the road and it runs on easy-glide castors. It's also got a high-speed spin drier.'

'Spin drier?' says Baxter, slugging clear liquid from a one-litre bottle labelled *Agua Minerale*. 'I'll only be interested if it's got a sin drier. Tell me this, if it's that good has it got a device to remove coins and pound notes from your trouser pockets when you put your stuff in the wash?'

John White, Brown's Tottenham team-mate, laughs and announces, 'Well I'm going to use my money to put a deposit down on a real car – a Ford Zephyr 6 – have you seen it? It's just out and it's got the nearest thing you'll see to tail fins in a British car. Nine hundred quid it costs and this money will take me a long way there.'

Hamilton, a new boy to international football, feels that his opening gambit of a twelve-guinea watch has now seen him outbid and, fearful of losing face, interjects, 'Well . . . well . . . a watch isn't all I'll be getting. We're going to get a modern gas fridge that gives you fresh food the whole year round and – and an Ilford camera, it takes pictures in ilfochrome thirty-two and . . .'

Baxter, who is now reclining with a sombrero over his face, tips back his hat, opens his eyes and says to Hamilton, 'Hey, Hammy, you don't need a gas fridge – you're full of gas already. And why are you talking about getting a cheap watch? I got one of those Lancos and I gave it away to a wean . . . it's like something that fell out of a lucky bag anyway. And you'd better watch that camera, it might burst when your bird tries to take a picture of your red face . . .' Hamilton hurdles several pairs of legs to launch himself at Baxter, who rapidly moves from a relaxed pose to an upright one with both arms extended. 'Come on, then . . .!' he shouts at Hamilton.

'Now, now boys,' Busby implores, sotto voce, stepping from the glass atrium at the rear of the hotel and starting to round the edge of the swimming pool. 'Remember, we've got a big match in a couple of days. Do you think the Yugoslavians will be fighting among themselves? Not a chance. Now I want you two to shake hands and then forget about all this.' Baxter and Hamilton shake, as requested.

'Right, all of you, on the beach in half an hour's time. I'll see you there for a training session so bring your sandshoes – the devil makes work for idle hands, indeed . . .'

· 1962 · 1962 · 1962 · 1962 · 1962 · 1962 · 1962 · 1962 · 1962 · 1962 ·

Busby stands back watching the training session on Viña del Mar's sandy beach; the players, he thinks, are lively and engaged again. Denis Law, though, appears to be lacking in energy. The forward has spent the past year at Torino where he has chafed against the strict discipline the Italians impose on footballers. Prior to the tournament, Busby appeared to have managed to sign him for Manchester United for a record £100,000 fee but Torino quickly reneged on that provisional agreement and insisted that the player was to be sold to rival Turin side, Juventus. The matter has dragged on, unresolved, for weeks, leaving Law unsettled. Hughie Andrews sums it up for the folks back home:

From a cosy wee Scots home to a sophisticated, gay, cosmopolitan world of wealth and luxury – it has been all too much for Denis. A lonely foreigner in a hostile country, he would be glad to say farewell to bodyguards, glamour and the

91

> high life if he gets his wish of leaving
> Italian shores. And that's despite the palatial,
> millionaire's flat in Turin's glitziest district.
> Perhaps the biggest blow was when Torino slashed
> his wages by a whopping fifty percent for being
> out at four in the morning and in a car crash
> with Joe Baker back in February. Torino like their
> boys to be tucked up snug in bed by ten o'clock.

Busby has agreed with Willie Allan not to involve any of his players in club business for the duration of the World Cup but it is clear to the keenly observant manager that the unresolved transfer is affecting Law. 'I'll go back on the trawlers like my father, in Aberdeen,' is all that the player has said to Busby on his insistence that he will refuse to allow Torino to manipulate his transfer to their city neighbours.

Following his observation of Law at the beach training session Busby places a call to Harold Hardman, chairman of Manchester United, telling him to inform Torino that the player will walk away from football rather than return to Italy and to increase simultaneously United's bid for Law by £10,000. 'That should do the trick,' Busby says, 'but don't mention my name in any of this. I guarantee you that he will score thirty goals for us next season. Oh, and I expect there will be a remuneration in this for me, having played my part in all this – but don't worry; we can discuss that when I return to Manchester after the World Cup. There's no rush.' He tells Hardman that if United's new transfer bid proves successful the chairman must phone Law with the news on the morning of the Yugoslavia match but must not mention Busby's role in the matter.

· 1962 · 1962 · 1962 · 1962 · 1962 · 1962 · 1962 · 1962 · 1962 · 1962 ·

'I was wrong to do that,' Baxter tells Busby, when the manager upbraids him for disguising a bottle filled with alcohol as *Agua Minerale*. He has been rumbled by Busby casually asking for, and wincing at, a sip from his poolside bottle. 'I was too big-headed,' Baxter adds. 'It won't happen again.'

'I thought we had agreed that you wouldn't touch the vodka again.' Busby says.

'I kept my word to you,' Baxter replies. 'I swear I did. It wasn't vodka. It was rum.'

· 1962 · 1962 · 1962 · 1962 · 1962 · 1962 · 1962 · 1962 · 1962 · 1962 ·

When the news of his tansfer to Manchester United comes through to Law he is like a man reborn. He hugs Busby and the manager, chortling, almost chokes on his pipe. The Yugoslavs, that afternoon, don't know what has hit them. Three minutes before half-time Henderson's corner floats across to Law, standing on the edge of the 'D' and, raising his left leg until it is almost parallel with the ground, he gives the ball an almighty dunt on the volley to whack it past Milutin Soskic in the Yugoslavia goal. Ten minutes into the second half, Law collects the ball midway inside the Yugoslavian half and, with unerring precision, his sharply taken, low, thirty-yard shot finds the narrowest of spaces between Soskic's fingertips and the inside of his left-hand post. A third goal arrives four minutes later when Hamilton spots Law's run and hits a precise pass through a Yugoslavian defence that has pushed up to the halfway line. Law streaks away down the left wing and when he reaches the edge of the eighteen-yard box he repositions his body, gets the ball onto his right foot and curls a cute, brilliantly accurate shot around the advancing Soskic. Scotland are in the World Cup final for the first time.

· 1962 · 1962 · 1962 · 1962 · 1962 · 1962 · 1962 · 1962 · 1962 · 1962 ·

It is Brazil, the world champions, whom Scotland will face in Santiago on 17 June 1962 at Chile's Estadio Nacional. Here there will be 70,000 spectators looking on, as opposed to the modest, friendly crowds at the previous venues for the Scots in Rancagua and Viña del Mar, where pelicans sometimes perched on the perimeter wall during matches. The daunting prospect of facing Brazil is diluted somewhat by the expected absence of their two most illustrious players: Pelé, who has missed most of the tournament due to a groin strain, and Garrincha, who was dismissed in Brazil's semi-final with Chile and is therefore in line for suspension for this, the subsequent match.

British press men from national titles have now descended on the Scots, England having been eliminated by Brazil in the quarter-finals. Busby enthuses to them about Baxter. 'When he hits a pass and you see the ball in the air, watch the markings and you will see it slow down as it reaches its target. That is how accurate, how precise he is. Off the field he is a gem as well, a good boy, a boy from a mining background – like myself. I've not had a minute's trouble from him since we've been here. I don't know where all these stories about him being a so-called "bad boy" come from.

'I have to say, I was sorry to see England go out,' Busby, the arch-diplomat, continues. 'It would have been nice to meet them – but we can't dwell on might-have-beens. This is a rare chance for us to win the trophy and I have to say that when I took over as Scotland manager I did so with the aim not only of reaching the final but, also, of winning the global tournament. Brazil will provide us with just as big a test as England could have done so we have to make sure we concentrate on the game in hand.'

Busby had been concerned at how the jump from cosy crowds of intrigued locals to a mammoth one, probably rooting for their fellow South Americans, in downtown Santiago might affect his players but by the time the coach carrying the Scotland team enters the environs of the Chilean capital, that concern has been displaced by another one. Baxter has, again, gone missing – he has not been seen for forty-eight hours – and the absence of their most creative player has had a dampening effect on the Scottish squad. With Garrincha, the tournament's outstanding player, and Pelé expected to be omitted from the Brazilian side, Baxter has the potential to press home the advantage for the Scots – but not if he is not around.

As the team coach nears the National Stadium, it slows to a crawl due to hundreds of Chileans cramming the streets to catch a glimpse of the World Cup finalists. For the inhabitants of this poverty stricken country, which is still recovering from the effects of the Valdivia earthquake in 1960, the tournament has brought an interval of fun and is a welcome relief from their daily struggles, not least because their own team reached the semi-finals, only for their adventure to end there in defeat to the Brazilians.

While the Scottish players smile and wave at the crowd, Busby is lost in thought. A man who presents to the world an impassive, unruffled persona, he is frequently in turmoil under the surface, constantly thinking matters over and questioning whether he has done the right thing in certain situations. Now, as he ponders the Baxter issue, he wonders if those in Manchester who have said that he has gone soft on players since the Munich Disaster, may just have a point. The theory being put about is that, having lost so many young men in that tragedy, he can no longer bring himself to be hard on other youngsters; seeing in them the spirit and hopes of those whose lives were snuffed out by the aircrash in West Germany. Does he really no longer have the heart to hand out the type of tough discipline that young foot-ballers sometimes require? Has his guilt over taking Manchester United into European football, leading to the subsequent tragedy, made him over sympathetic toward those such as Baxter, in whom he sees reflected the light of life, now gone out, that shone in his Busby Babes? Did he take the right tack with Baxter? Should he have been harder on him?

As Busby chews on the tip of his little finger, looking downwards – an introverted mannerism characteristic of him when deep in thought – Pat Crerand rouses him, 'Boss, boss, he's here!' Crerand yells. Busby glances in the direction Crerand is pointing and there is Baxter, astride a blue Vespa being steered by a young, brown-skinned girl, she in a flimsy yellow dress and Baxter in a pair of tomato-red shorts and multi-coloured, open-necked shirt, both arms free, mouth agape, screaming at his team-mates on the coach while holding up a wad of cash – the proceeds from another trip to the El Niño Loco casino. Busby turns around and sees that the rest of the players are on their feet, laughing at the sheer front of their team-mate. If the World Cup in its latter stages is a test of nerve, then, Busby has to admit, Baxter has just done a marvellous job of lifting tension from the Scotland squad. Repercussions will have to wait until later. There is a World Cup waiting to be won. Baxter will be in Busby's team.

· 1962 · 1962 · 1962 · 1962 · 1962 · 1962 · 1962 · 1962 · 1962 · 1962 ·

Half an hour to go before kick-off and Busby leaves the Scotland dressing room to allow the players breathing space to get on with their preparations. A new anxiety is preying on his mind; such is the lot of the football manager. Brazil have not yet submitted their team lines and Busby, irritated by the delay, sallies forth to find a FIFA official who may be able to help him. A Chilean FA man scurries away as he sees Busby approach – the official looks panicked and is holding both hands, palms upward, out in front of him as if to say he does not wish to be drawn into anything. Busby senses something is going on and hurries to seek out an English-speaker. Among the officials milling around in the area outside the dressing rooms he locates Gert de Vlinder, from the Belgian FA. 'I've not seen an actual team sheet on paper,' de Vlinder tells Busby, 'but – and you're not going to like this – Garrincha is in.'

'What?' Busby says. 'But he was sent off in the semi-final – he can't play in the final.'

Less than twenty minutes remain before kick-off when Busby finally manages to locate Bob Kelly, the SFA president, and Willie Allan, both standing just outside the main stand, each enjoying a cigarette without a care in the world. 'Well, we can't go against FIFA,' Allan says, when Busby informs him of the situation. 'What do you suggest we do? Scratch from a World Cup final with 70,000 fans in the stadium? There would be a riot, our name would be mud and I'm sure they would give the cup to Brazil.'

Busby ruminates. 'You're probably right. But imagine if the boot was on the other foot. Do you think the Brazilians would take this lying down?'

Allan stubs out his cigarette. 'No, I doubt that they would, Matt,' he says, 'but you know how it is.'

As it transpires, Allan had been made aware of Garrincha's inclusion long before Busby. On Allan's arrival at the stadium he had been informed by FIFA that Garrincha would play and was simultaneously warned that if Scotland were to kick up any sort of a fuss over this, they could face a ban from world football; not only that but Allan could, also, forget completely about any prospect of a place on one of FIFA's international committees. The SFA secretary has, as FIFA had anticipated, proved unwilling to untangle this particular web of FIFA politics, which, in South America, has broken the bounds of football to touch high-level government.

FIFA's permission to Brazil to field Garrincha in the final is the result of a tortuous series of events. The linesman who officiated at the semi-final between Brazil and Chile left the country the morning after the semi and was thus unavailable to offer evidence as to why he had advised the referee to dismiss Garrincha in that match. With the linesman absent, FIFA has decreed that Garrincha should be pardoned and allowed to participate in the final, even though all five other players dismissed in the 1962 tournament have been given one-match suspensions. The linesman has, in fact, been whisked away by a shadowy figure on the fringes of the Brazilian party who offered him an airline ticket and a holiday in Paris on condition that he leave before the committee met.

It seems appropriate, then, that Salvador Dali, no stranger

to the surreal, his eyes and moustache twirling, should be among the spectators in the National Stadium as the teams climb the stairs from their subterranean dressing rooms and emerge for the final of the 1962 World Cup. 'Baxter explodes into a match,' Dali says, 'with the beauty of a mushroom cloud after a nuclear explosion.'

There is an apprehensiveness about some of the Scottish players as they come to terms with the idea that Garrincha will, after all, be facing them. A herd of photographers, one hundred-strong, some stretched out on the ground, some on their haunches, form a crescent moon around the Scottish players and jostle to get the best team picture of the Scots before kick-off. As this is going on, the Brazilians nonchalantly perform audacious tricks with the ball as part of their elaborate warm-up. The Scottish players are not used to such attention from the media but it is quickly put into perspective. Once they have the Scots' team picture in the bag, the photographers swarm, like angry bees, to snap each and every Brazilian player, not as a team but individually.

Pelé, in a white, V neck, cricket-style sweater for chilly Chile, is, as expected, on the sidelines, signing autographs, but there on the wing is Garrincha, the star of the tournament. The player's legs are noticeably crooked – his left leg bends out and his right leg bends in – but this, far from stinting his career has advanced it: opponents find it impossible to predict the direction in which he is likely to move. That, added to his mesmeric ball control and trickery, makes him gloriously elusive on the pitch. 'What planet is Garrincha from?' Chile's *Mercurio* newspaper asked after the host nation's 4–2 defeat in the semis. As the photographers encircle him, he jogs on the spot, arms spread wide as if to say, 'Here I am; I'm the guy you've all come to see; I'm the star of the show.'

Fourteen minutes of cautious sparring have passed when Gordon Smith, the Scotland outside-right, gracefully controls a ball from Baxter, evades a flailing boot and nicks it inside to Denis Law who shapes to shoot but, instead, nicks it to John White, on the edge of the Brazil eighteen-yard box.

White darts into the penalty area, the ball now on his left foot, and only Djalma Santos, the right-back, is in place to make a challenge, which he does, just as White lifts a delicate, flicked, precise ball into the path of Davie Wilson, haring into the area from the left wing. The winger's first-time shot, hit with the outside of the boot, curls around Gylmar dos Santos, the Brazil goalkeeper, and plants itself pleasingly in the far corner of the net. As one, the 70,000 inside the stadium rise to acclaim an exceptional goal from an exceptional team. Scotland, incredibly, are a goal up on the world champions in the World Cup final.

Two minutes later, Smith plays an angled, diagonal pass in to Law, who chests it cleverly into the path of St John, who uses the laces to control the ball and take it away from Zito, the centre-back, then flies after the ball into the space he has carved out for himself but Gylmar gets to it a fraction before the Scot can nudge it into the net. The game settles back down until, with twenty-five minutes gone, Amarildo, Pelé's replacement, draws Hamilton, Crerand and McNeill toward him before veering away from all three in the direction of the goal-line. Off-balance and with the ball only just in play, the Brazil inside-left appears to have little option but to cross and, in anticipation of that, Brown takes a couple of steps backward just as Amarildo hits a swerving shot inside the goalkeeper's near post for a stunning equalizer. Both sides, again, take a step back after this and with Caldow and McNeill paying special attention to Garrincha and successfully tying him down, a game between two evenly matched teams reaches half-time.

It is not all artistry with the Brazilians. Shortly after the interval, Law latches onto the ball midway inside the Brazil half and as the Scot tries to dig it out from his feet, Mauro goes through him like a dose of salts, freeing Didi to run hard at a sagging Scottish midfield and retreating defence. His pass to Amarildo sends Hamilton tumbling to the ground in his efforts to cut out the ball and Brown, now wary of the Brazilian's potency as a goal-scorer, rushes to his right-hand post. Amarildo shapes to shoot with his left foot but instead dummies McNeill and instantaneously uses his right boot to chip the ball to the back post where the inrushing Zito heads it down and into the net.

The contest ends in disastrous fashion for Scotland. With twelve minutes remaining and Baxter, Crerand and Law all having gone close to an equalizer, Brazil again mix up their styles of play. Djalma Santos, midway inside the Scottish half, and on the wing, volleys a high, hopeful, long ball into the heart of the Scotland penalty area; the sort of tactic one might expect to find in the Scottish Second Division, albeit executed in this instance with terrific precision. Brown advances to collect the ball but the high, Chilean sun gets in his eyes and when he drops the ball, Vava is on hand to prod it into the net. Brown, disconsolate, stares at the ground and throws down his peaked goalkeeper's cap, useless as a defence against the sun just at the very moment when he had needed it most.

'We are pleased that we gave a good account of ourselves,' Busby says afterwards. 'And we attach no blame to Bill Brown. He has been outstanding throughout this tournament and had it not been for him, we would not have been here today to share in this glorious occasion. He is blameless – and I can vouch that all the lads agree on that.

'No, we do not feel aggrieved that Garrincha was allowed to play in this match, even though we had to make allowances to deal with his talents. Indeed, we would have preferred it if Pelé, too, had been fit and ready to compete. We want to win against the strongest opposition in a good contest and today Brazil, even minus Pelé, proved stronger than us. With a player like Amarildo as a ready replacement, Brazil were hardly weakened by the loss of Pelé. As we leave this wonderful country, we would only like to thank graciously the Chilean people for their kind hospitality throughout the time we have been here. We are pleased to have reached the World Cup final and though we have fallen short in our ambition of taking the trophy, it is quite an achievement to have come this far in the tournament. After all, who knows when a Scottish team will be next in a World Cup final?'

LION HEARTS

'What about them, eh?' Jock Stein's brusque words are accompanied by a sour grimace of disgust as he slaps down the morning papers in front of his players as they breakfast lightly at the Hendon Hall Hotel in north London. The low murmur of conversation ceases immediately as the Scotland team's attention is caught by their manager's grim mood on the morning of the biggest game in which the nation has ever been involved; one that is bigger even than the 1962 final. A procession of players make their way to the table on which Stein has deposited a copy of every morning paper, southern English editions all, with their headlines and stories tempered to please their audience. 'It's the Jockney Final' is the headline on the back page of the *Daily Express*, whose Reg Drury

– 'straight from Drury Lane', Stein mutters – informs his readers:

> This is the final every Englishman wanted. Two for
> the price of one and you can't get better value
> than that at Wembley market on a Saturday after-
> noon, can you? Yes, this is the chance for England
> to lift the World Cup that has been destined for
> the hands of Bobby Moore ever since Alf Ramsey
> stated on the very day he took over as England
> manager four years ago, 'England will win the
> World Cup in 1966.' At the same time, Moore and
> his men can slap down these Scots once and for
> all . . .

Every newspaper follows a similar line, all the way up to the rarefied view offered by Lancelot St-John Pirat, the *Daily Telegraph*'s 'association football' correspondent:

> Even John Buchan, a native Scot, but an eminently
> logical one, would find it inconceivable that
> England might ascend the thirty-nine steps to the
> Royal Box late this afternoon vanquished by a
> Scotland side for whom it is a triumph just to
> be taking the field for the final.

St-John Pirat then goes on to invoke with stunning historical inaccuracy the spirit of the Battle of Trafalgar and even attempts to make a light joke of Culloden, while the *Guardian* corre-spondent writes:

> Thirty-six years ago on this very day, Uruguay
> became the first nation to lift the World Cup
> trophy. It would be slightly unfair to describe it
> as a hollow victory but with England absent from
> that first tournament, their triumph lacked a

certain je ne sais quoi. Today, the nation that gave
the world the game has the chance to lift a trophy
that has grown greatly in stature since those
early days and most especially since the Football
Association decided to grace the new international
tournament with England's presence from 1950
onwards. An England victory will be welcomed around
the world as giving the World Cup a certain
completeness, a certain authentication. With the
weight of such history-in-the-making bearing down
upon them, this modest Scotland team, which has
surprised everyone by squeezing into the final,
looks incapable of bearing up under the strain.

While the Scottish players read paper after paper, Jock Stein, who has been hovering about on the edge of the room watching their reactions, quietly drifts out of the door and leaves them to digest and discuss the news.

1966 · 1966 · 1966 · 1966 · 1966 · 1966 · 1966 · 1966 · 1966 · 1966 ·

As his players sit in the Wembley dressing room prior to the match Stein moves among them, making only the odd comment of encouragement, one to one. Denis Law, staring at the floor, emits stern resolve; Billy Bremner is a tightly coiled ball of fury; and Stein even turns a blind eye when Jim Baxter, the midfield player, disappears into the toilet and emerges slightly flushed thanks to having consumed 'a wee nip' to warm him for the contest ahead. Law suddenly shouts, 'Boys, I play against these blokes week in, week out and let me tell you, you've got nothing to fear from them. Get out there and get into them.'

Stein now takes a couple of steps into the centre of the dressing room, looks at his watch and then looks up and says, 'Now, you've made history – you've got us to a second World Cup final; two in a row. Nobody expected it so you've done everything and more in terms of what was demanded of you. You are legends now, legends in ten minutes when the game starts and legends, no matter what happens, when this match finishes. I'll ask from you only one thing – go out there and play to your capabilities. Do that and we'll be all right.'

When the two teams line up in the tunnel, Nobby Stiles, the England midfield player, trots across to shake Law's hand but is shrugged away with a fierce glare.

'Give me the ball and we'll take it from there, no bother,' Baxter yells so that the English can hear, loud and clear. 'Let's show these people what it's all about.'

Soon, insults are being exchanged freely, with players who are club-mates noising up each other mercilessly. The tunnel at Wembley, sloping upward gently, reveals to the players, as they move toward their destiny, a sea of Lion Rampant flags, blending with union flags. There are so many Scottish standards that it feels like the next best thing to a home match for the players in navy blue shirts.

Bobby Moore, the England captain, wins the toss and opts to give the kick-off to the Scots. Law taps the ball to Charlie Cooke and, with 400 million pairs of eyes watching on television around the world and 97,000 British onlookers inside the stadium, the 1966 World Cup final is underway.

The opening minutes see both sides moving the ball forward quickly and the match has about it the urgency of a domestic cup tie rather than the patient, probing pace often characteristic of international football. A low, twenty-five-yard shot from 'Sir' Roger Hunt, the England striker, tests Bobby Ferguson in the Scotland goal but he holds the ball confidently. He finds Tommy Gemmell with his throw and the left-back streaks majestically past Alan Ball, the England midfield player. As George Cohen, the England right-back, advances on Gemmell, the Scot nicks the ball neatly to Bobby Lennox on the left wing, who is now in space as Jack Charlton comes lumbering out from central defence, like a panicked giant giraffe, and collides into the Scotland winger. Both players sprawl on the turf and the game is held up for several minutes. Charlton gets slowly to his feet, limping heavily, though whether this – and his extended spell on the deck – is to try to evade the referee's censure is unclear.

Play resumes and when Stiles's cross from the right is headed clear by Billy McNeill, it only goes as far as Bobby Charlton, the England midfield player, who directly pitches the ball back into the heart of the Scottish penalty area. As Ferguson rises to meet the cross he is clattered by Geoff Hurst, the England striker and his West Ham team-mate, and Ferguson lies flat out, dazed by the impact of the collision. Hurst finds himself engulfed by booing on his own home territory. At a time when substitute goalkeepers are unimaginable it is a worrying moment for the Scots, but Ferguson gets to his feet, clutching his mouth after his encounter with thirteen stones of hurled Hurst. 'It was as if a sack o' tatties had come flying off the back of a lorry and walloped me right on the kisser,' the Ardrossan man will later say of that unnerving moment.

The Queen, in the Royal Box, looks on expressionless. Are her loyalties swinging Balmoral or Windsor way? Or is she that rare thing, a neutral at this final?

Wembley is far from being alien territory to these Scots. Schoolboy internationals, FA Cup finals and the annual Scotland–England international mean that almost all of them have played here before. 'This is my London Palladium,' Baxter has said before the final. 'If I can't turn it on here, I need my backside kicked.' The Scotland national side has indeed often found it easier to play here than at Hampden. Venturing south to Wembley for the biennial encounter with the Auld Enemy engenders the same emotions the players feel in major matches at the World Cup finals. So, now that their latest trip to Wembley combines not only a match in the finals but also the final itself and with England as their opponents, it is not intimidating at all as a venue; more one that feels almost like the home of a posh old friend and rival, a shade more refined than one's own rickety old base, and a place where it is necessary to show oneself to best effect.

For the older Scots fans, the place evokes welcome memories: of the Wembley Wizards, the 1928 side with its diminutive forward line, who went to bed and prayed for rain the night before facing England, found their prayers answered in the morning and won 5–1 on a slick surface suited to refined ball-players. It's the venue associated with 'Last-minute Reilly', the Hibernian striker of the fifties, who seemed to score with ease against the English, often in the dying seconds and especially on their home turf.

Everything about playing at Wembley fills the Scottish players with anticipation – other venues cannot conjure up quite the same willingness among them to shine, to take risks, to indulge in derring-do; at old, familiar Hampden the pressure is greater because of the expectation for the team to win at will when at home. Wembley is more welcoming; with its pristine pitch and grand ambience, it is truly loved by the Scottish players. It is as if they are a bunch of children from an orphanage on an annual day out to a grand old aristocratic stately pile; one that is taken for granted by its residents but which the visitors fall upon eagerly, gambolling on the manicured lawns with a degree of abandon never seen in those who have the privilege of being able to savour its magnificent facilities all year round.

· 1966 · 1966 · 1966 · 1966 · 1966 · 1966 · 1966 · 1966 · 1966 · 1966 ·

With twelve minutes gone, Scotland spurt upfield at speed and Lennox crosses from the left toward Denis Law, inside the English penalty area. The ball goes too long for the Scotland forward and loops over him, toward Ray Wilson, the England left-back. He goes to make a simple, clearing header but he is falling backward and slightly off-balance so, when he does meet the ball he cannot obtain any power or distance on it and instead cushions it softly down to the feet of Jimmy Johnstone, the Scotland outside-right, fifteen yards from goal and at an angle. The winger shows immense composure to control the ball quickly and get a right-footed shot away as Bobby Moore slams in a swift challenge. The ball is not cleanly struck but it is directed well away from Gordon Banks, the England goalkeeper, who is unable to move quickly enough to prevent it rolling into the corner of his goal – and Scotland are 1–0 ahead. The noise from the terraces is ear-shattering, the Lion Rampants are unfurled again and Johnstone, right arm raised in triumph, accepts the congratulations of his team-mates before strutting back boldly to his own half where he takes up his position on the touchline in front of Stein and Ramsey, both of whom remain seated on their respective benches, equally impassive.

Scotland exude confidence, rolling the ball around in style, but England soon begin to edge their way back into the game. Billy Bremner fouls Moore midway inside the Scotland half, after eighteen minutes, and the England captain, looking to gather the ball to take a quick free-kick, finds that Gottfried Dienst, the Swiss referee, gets there before him and aids Moore by shuffling the ball quickly with his feet to the Englishman, allowing Moore to scoop it swiftly into the centre of the Scottish penalty area even before the defence can ready itself. Hurst, aware of what Moore, his club-mate, is planning, makes a fast, diagonal run into the box to meet the ball and even though Ferguson is alive to the intentions of his West Ham colleagues and shuttles across his goal-line quickly, Hurst's header proves too powerful for the goalkeeper, still slightly groggy from the centre-forward's earlier hefty challenge, and the ball slips past his outstretched arm and inside his right-hand post for the equalizer.

As half-time approaches, a flurry of action has the crowd enthralled. A mistake by Cohen sees England concede a corner. Lennox takes it from the right and Gemmell meets the ball on the volley, powering in a twenty-yard shot that is heading for Banks's top right-hand corner. The goalkeeper pushes the ball away but it falls to Law, whose half-hit effort is parried by Banks. The ball bounces menacingly inside the English six-yard box, like a live hand grenade, before several England defenders converge on it quickly and Jackie Charlton whacks it clear. Scottish forwards hold their heads in hands at this precious, missed opportunity to regain the lead but Bremner goes around his team-mates individually, exhorting them to redouble their efforts. Baxter, until this point a lazy-looking, peripheral figure, finds his captain to be particularly animated in his 'chat' with him.

· 1966 · 1966 · 1966 · 1966 · 1966 · 1966 · 1966 · 1966 · 1966 · 1966 ·

It is a lively Scottish dressing room at the interval. The players are outraged at Dienst allowing Hurst to get away with his challenge on Ferguson, who is still feeling its after-effects but who must continue for the second forty-five minutes. The defenders agree among themselves that they will fight even harder to protect their goalkeeper and the manager stays in the background, happy to allow the players to get their feelings off their chests. Stein always enjoys seeing his players riled; he believes it intensifies their concentration and makes them more determined to win. It is only as the ten-minute break draws near to its close that he addresses the team as a whole.

'So do you think that first half went well?' he asks them. The players look at him, aware that Stein will have assessed the flow of the game expertly and that he is unlikely to be genuinely seeking their opinion on the performance of the team. 'Well?' he says. 'What did you think? Did you think you played well? I think you did. I thought you all did very well.' The players, relieved, relax after the momentary tension induced by the possibility that Stein had been about to criticize them after a first half in which they have given everything only to be thwarted, in their eyes, by some poor refereeing. Some now drain the last dregs of their traditional

British cup of half-time tea; others tighten their tie-ups in preparation for the resumption of action; one or two get to their feet and perform stretching exercises. They presume that Stein has said all he has to say until he adds, 'Not everyone thinks the same, mind you.' They look at their manager, quizzically. 'I'm telling you,' Stein goes on. 'You know that Kenneth Wolstenholme, the commentator? Right, well, he's on the BBC, telling the English, he's telling the world . . . that you're finished, that you've put on a "jolly good show" in the first half and that England are going to go on and have you well beaten, easy, just like that. He says you've played better than anybody could have expected and that it will still be no disgrace when you eventually lose to this great England team. He is saying that he thinks it's all over . . . and that it is, now.'

The players' mood is now one of anger as they take to the tunnel for the second half, leaving Stein smiling to himself in the dressing room before he returns to the manager's bench. Wolstenholme, the BBC's well-spoken football commentator, a former RAF man, up on his television gantry, contentedly munching a slice of Genoa cake and pouring a cup of Earl Grey tea from his silver flask, has said no such thing, made no such implication.

· 1966 · 1966 · 1966 · 1966 · 1966 · 1966 · 1966 · 1966 · 1966 · 1966 ·

The weather has been changeable all afternoon and as the teams take to the turf for the second half, they are greeted by a heavy downpour. It has rained heavily for the previous two days, softening up the pitch, which is now beginning to cut up badly, especially in and around the penalty areas. The players appear far from leg-weary, though, as they begin the second forty-five minutes at the same lung-bursting pace they have maintained throughout the first period. The brightest moment in the early stages of the second half does not, though, come courtesy of the players but from Mr Dienst, who is proving a rather eccentric figure to be in charge of a World Cup final. Stiles bounces the ball off the turf in frustration at the award of a free-kick to Scotland and as the ball drops groundward, Mr Dienst gets his head to it – to the great pleasure of the crowd – and nods it to Bremner before giving Stiles a strong, finger-pointing lecture.

Baxter is now a livelier presence, especially when, eight minutes into the second half, he moves on to Gilzean's cute pass inside the penalty area to turn a shot toward goal. Banks half-smothers it but cannot prevent the ball squirming under his body and into the side netting. Lennox takes the corner, which is cleared only to the edge of the penalty area, where Law sways left and right in front of Peters before shooting. The ball takes a slight deflection as it hurtles through the crowded penalty area and this wrong-foots Jack Charlton, limping slightly after his early, clumsy challenge on Lennox.

Instead of clearing the ball with his right boot, as he intends, Charlton can only block it with his left, sending it spinning up into the air. It drops perfectly for Baxter, one of three Scots who have eagerly converged on the area around the penalty spot, awaiting this piece of manna from heaven. Baxter does not make clean contact with his volley but the ball flies between Banks and Wilson on the goal-line to make it 2–1 to Scotland. Baxter trots away to acknowledge the crowd and every Scottish player other than Ferguson converges on him to offer their congratulations.

Two minutes later, Lennox pelts down the left wing, hurdles

a high and hefty challenge from George Cohen, hits the touch-line, skips back inside a sliding challenge from Bobby Moore and whips a fast, low ball across the face of goal. Favourite to get to the ball is Jack Charlton but Baxter is too clever, too precise, for the lumbering defender, and nicks it off his toe, draws the ball under the sole of his boot and pirouettes before cheekily back-heeling the ball over the England goal-line. With less than an hour played of the 1966 World Cup final, Scotland are 3–1 ahead and hugely in control of the match.

As Baxter walks back toward his own half, he reaches to the waistband of his shorts and produces a piece of pink, rectangular paper, a betting slip, and exaggeratedly mimics checking the score against the huge electronic scoreboard behind the goal before raising his right hand to give a thumbs-up sign. Alan Ball, bristling with anger, races toward the Scot to give him a mouthful but Baxter flaps his fingers together in imitation of a yapping jaw before Moore draws away his team-mate. The England captain still jabs a warning finger in Baxter's direction. Scotland have a good, solid lead but it still seems too early to suggest that all bets are off, especially when goading dangerous, spirited opposition in such a fashion.

· 1966 · 1966 · 1966 · 1966 · 1966 · 1966 · 1966 · 1966 · 1966 · 1966 ·

Scotland have sailed through this tournament with ease; a collection of fine players growing in confidence with each passing match due to their gradual progress from north to south. It has helped that their group games were played in the north-east of England and the style that they displayed in victories over Chile and North Korea, followed by a draw with the Soviet Union, got the Middlesbrough people onside and wishing them well as they progressed to a quarter-final with Hungary in Sunderland; the locals got right behind the Scots as Baxter, star of the Roker Park club for the past season, inspired a swaggering 3–0 victory. The semi-final in Liverpool produced even greater backing for the Scots; West Germany were never likely to win a popularity contest in a city that had been bombed to bits during the war and with Bill Shankly, the Liverpool manager, whipping up local support for the Scotland team in the days prior to the match, Goodison Park willed them on to a testing, nerve-shredding 2–1 victory over the Germans, the decisive goal an eighty-ninth minute Law header.

On watching England's semi-final with Portugal, on the night after Scotland's win over the Germans, Baxter retires to the Long Bar inside Wembley long before the ninety minutes are up and tells a couple of friendly Scottish journalists, 'Imagine that lot winning the World Cup. We can't let it happen.'

· 1966 · 1966 · 1966 · 1966   1966 · 1966 · 1966 · 1966 · 1966 · 1966 ·

There is never any room for complacency in an England–Scotland match. A team can be ahead and look as though they are cruising to victory when – bam – they can find their billowing sails suddenly sagging and powerless. On the hour at Wembley, with Baxter, Alex Hamilton and Jimmy Johnstone combining for the latest in a series of attacks on the England goal, Bobby Moore latches onto the ball inside his own penalty area and, with Jack Charlton screaming at his captain to belt it into the terraces, Moore instead takes a touch before smoothing a cool, fifty-yard pass across the halfway line. Hurst, cheeks puffed out like an overgrown, particularly ugly cherub, goes galloping off in pursuit of the ball, with Billy McNeill the only Scotland defender in attendance. On and on pounds Hurst, doggedly knocking the ball ahead of him with each heavy, carthorse-at-full-pelt-like stride, until he reaches the edge of the eighteen-yard box, from where he swipes a cannon-ball-strength shot high into the roof of Ferguson's net.

England press for the equalizer and their chance arrives when Ball, for the first time in the match, gets the better of Gemmell, driving outside him and, in a flurry of limbs, reaches the bye-line, from where he cuts the ball back diagonally in the direction of Hurst, hovering on the corner of the six-yard box. The centre-forward, back to goal, cleverly controls the ball on his right instep, driving it down into the ground so that it bounces perfectly for him to wheel and volley in one movement. The ball streaks toward goal, rising rapidly and cracks off the underside of the bar before rebounding down and out without crossing the line. McNeill gets to it first and, arms spread wide, elegantly heads the ball up and over the crossbar and behind for a corner.

Despite the clear evidence that the ball was not in, the English players claim wildly for a goal, surrounding Dienst and appealing to his linesman. Dienst, who has been behind the play, flounders temporarily, not sure what to do; he is aware that with Stanley Rous, an Englishman, as president of FIFA, a failure to award a goal could blight his career for good but, equally, that his reputation as a referee and continued appointments to big matches on big occasions could be compromised by making the wrong decision. His eyes hungrily and relievedly alight on the figure of Tofik Bakhramov, his linesman, from the Soviet Union, who makes the eccentric Dienst look like a model of sobriety. Bakhramov, a tall, stick-thin figure, with a shock of straying, wild, grey hair, tooth-brush moustache, permanently startled expression and with a thin white belt holding up his black shorts, has the slightly distracted air of a garret-constricted artist out for a rare stroll in the fresh air, and as Dienst approaches him, he is nodding his head up and down rapidly. Dienst reaches him, referee and linesman confer head to head, and Dienst nods agree-ment with Bakhramov, before the Swiss, whistle in mouth, returns to the edge of the penalty area and points to the corner arc, motioning Ball to resume play with a corner-kick.

It is a moment of mixed feelings for Bakhramov. An Azerbaijani who fought the Germans on the front line during the Second World War, he had, prior to the semi-final, resolved that if the West Germans got there and a key decision fell to him, he would give it against them in revenge. With the Scots it is different. His war memories are of the 'kilted ladies from hell' who had fought so fiercely against the common enemy and with whom he had happily fraternised in the final days of the conflict. Still, he feels disappointment at being denied his chance to extract a modicum of personal revenge upon the Germans.

Little Alan Ball now lets loose his emotion, turning from Dienst to Bakhramov and screaming in protest at the offi-cials' failure to award the goal. Baxter ambles up to him. 'Hey, Ball,' he says to the diminutive figure with the thatch of red hair. 'See you, you could nearly be a Scotsman. You look like a Scotsman and you can scream and shout like one but you wouldnae get in this team – because you're no bliddy good.' The England man looks ready to lose the place completely now and advances in Baxter's direction, yelling threats, in his high-pitched voice, at his opponent. 'Hey, Billy,' Baxter shouts to Bremner. 'We've got Jimmy Clitheroe here and I think his voice is about to break. Either that or he wants his mammy.'

The corner duly taken and cleared by the Scottish defence, the game resumes with a Scotland break, the ball shuttled swiftly from Gemmell to Bremner and on to Charlie Cooke who, seeing Baxter advance into the English half, picks out the midfield player with a neat pass. Baxter, as always, hugely aware of everything that is happening on the field of play, has noticed that every England player, as per Alf Ramsey's instructions, is now behind the ball and so, instead of progressing the move toward the English goal, he instead turns and moves back into his own half. The English players – nicknamed 'Ramsey's Robots' by the Scots, and not programmed to comprehend the unusual or the unorthodox – stand agape, not following Baxter, sure that he is going to turn and bring play back in their direction. No; instead, Baxter continues to head toward his own goal and eases between Gemmell and McNeill and back into his own penalty area, where he faces Ferguson. On reaching the corner of the six-yard box, he draws back his left foot and pings an angled shot toward goal from the same spot from which Hurst had his unsuccessful and much-disputed scoring attempt a couple of minutes earlier. The ball clips the underside of the bar and bounces down just in front of the line, à la Hurst. Baxter controls it and then turns to the crowd, largely English people in this section of the stadium, arms spread wide, and shrugs, as if to say, 'See – the ball doesn't go in if you do that.' Booing ensues so he looks at them quizzically, has a quick glance around, to make sure there are still no England players near, and then clips the ball off the same spot on the underside of the bar, again watches it land just in front of the goal-line and again turns to the crowd, raising his arms to them even more emphatically, with palms spread wide, as if to say, 'Does that not prove it?'

Ball, furious, is now pounding toward Baxter, crazed with humiliation, disappointment and anger and, even though Baxter has his back to him and the ball is on the other side of his body from the Englishman, Ball, from half a dozen yards away, launches into a two-footed 'tackle', studs up, ready to extract a smidgeon of revenge for the events of the past few minutes. Baxter merely flicks the ball in the air and jumps along with it, leaving Ball to go piling into a phalanx of photographers, wildly scattering equipment and the snappers' folding stools. Baxter taps the ball to McNeill and throws his head back, roaring with laughter. 'Hey, you're a picture now!' he shouts in the direction of the photographer-submerged Ball before trotting up the field again.

'I thought you could play the game a bit,' Hurst says to Baxter, as he passes the forward, trying to goad the Scot. 'Why do you not play some football, Jock?' In response, Baxter laughs and then replies, 'Do you know what, Geoffrey, old boy? That's a jolly good idea!'

He asks for the ball from Bremner, who is holding possession inside the centre circle. Baxter takes his pass, sidesteps a wan challenge from Martin Peters and, having found himself a bit of space, chips the ball into the air and then proceeds to play keepie-uppie, reaching eight before Cohen advances to challenge him. Baxter simply flicks the ball over the full-back's head and into the penalty area, where Denis Law latches onto it, with the alacrity of a cobra hungry for prey, and cracks a low shot under the body of Gordon Banks to make it 4–2 to Scotland.

· 1966 · 1966 · 1966 · 1966 · 1966 · 1966 · 1966 · 1966 · 1966 · 1966 ·

Alf Ramsey, the England manager, sits impassively on the bench, despite the deficit. He passes on some tactical instructions for Harold Shepherdson, his assistant, to give to the players but Ramsey realizes, as a football man through and through, that with only twenty minutes remaining, the game is slipping away fast from his team. It should be the ultimate defeat – Ramsey's image is of the steadfast, stiff, southern Englishman – but how the Wembley crowd would be surprised if they knew Ramsey's true feelings at that moment. Wistfully, he is lamenting how much he would like to be on the opposite managerial bench and how close he came to clinching the position of Scotland manager.

During his playing career with Southampton and Tottenham Hotspur, rumours had abounded in the football world that the olive-skinned Ramsey was of gypsy stock. Ramsey, of humble origins in Dagenham, near London, has felt no shame in this but, on becoming manager of Ipswich Town, has made it his business to trace, as far as possible, his roots and, in doing so, has discovered that his great-grandfather, one Rab Ramsey, a Highland Games champion, hailed from Portsoy in Banffshire. Having won the Football League championship with Ipswich Town in 1962, Ramsey, looking to step up to international management, had then discreetly approached Willie Allan, the Scottish Football Association's secretary, with a request to be considered for the post of Scotland manager, following Matt Busby's decision to return, full-time, to the management of Manchester United. Ramsey, in support of his application, stressed his admiration for the Scottish style of play and his newfound Scottish lineage. Allan is impressed but, after taking some weeks to turn the matter over in his mind, has informed Ramsey that, impressive as he is as a man and as a manager, he feels it would regrettably be unacceptable to the Scottish supporters to have a former England international in charge of their cherished team. Weeks later, in October 1962, Ramsey is appointed England manager by a Football Association entirely unaware of his previous intention to defect.

The England manager, in subsequent years, has over-compensated for his disappointment at failing to land the Scotland job by presenting himself as the archetype of the buttoned-up Englishman, even affecting an upper-class accent that he feels matches his promotion to the officer class in service of his country. He also becomes well known for what seems to be an open dislike of the Scots but which is really a public expression of his channelling his feelings of frustration at not landing the one managerial post he desired above all others.

How Ramsey envies Jock Stein! Ramsey, for all that he admires the professionalism and dedication of the players at his disposal, knows that, with the odd, rare exception, such as Bobby Charlton, his key midfield player, they cannot match for inventiveness, style, imagination and inspiration the players that the Scots seem to produce as a matter of routine. Having witnessed Baxter's audacious performance at Wembley today, he would give anything for a player with such chutzpah. Looking at his two tough but fairly predictable full-backs, he thinks about what he could do with Gemmell and Hamilton, the quick and exciting, raiding Scots, working with such speed and adaptability that they are almost supplementary wingers; the former with a long-range shot that most strikers would find hard to match. Then there are the traditionally diminutive Scottish wingers themselves, in this instance Lennox and

Johnstone, players for whom the unpredictable seems a matter of routine and against whom it is impossible for Ramsey to devise a strategy; so denuded of natural creativity is the England manager that he has done away with wingers altogether. Ramsey has also scoured the country seeking an English goal-scorer capable of replicating the skills of Denis Law, a stylish finisher but one also possessed of toughness and aggression; but no Englishman can combine those qualities with the same degree of panache as Law. Then there is Billy Bremner, a midfield player in whom are blended supreme ball-playing skills with a fiercely competitive and aggressive ability to win the ball and close down opponents; English midfield players tend to be either ball-playing artists or hard men and never a combination of both. The Scots appear to have the blueprint for this type of player and, as far a Ramsey can see, roll them off some mysterious Highland production line. This is one reason why Ramsey, a true aficionado of football, had wanted the job of Scottish manager; so that he could get to the root of the mystery of how the Scots, year after year, produce players of such sterling pedigree.

Ramsey has done his best with the players at his disposal; he really has. He has recognized that they lack the flair to play with wingers and so has stressed work-rate, organization and togetherness. He deserves enormous credit for taking his team all the way to the final but, with Scotland having won three and lost only one of the past five annual home internationals between the two nations, Ramsey has never been deceived, like so many other Englishmen, into thinking that his team were favourites to win the final. He would never tell anyone but the match is actually going exactly the way that, all along, he had always feared.

· 1966 · 1966 · 1966 · 1966 · 1966 · 1966 · 1966 · 1966 · 1966 · 1966 ·

With ten minutes remaining, Cooke takes possession of the ball on the right wing, ten yards in from the touchline. He looks for Johnstone on his outside but instead his eye is caught by the sight of a rumpled figure, a small, stocky man in horn-rimmed spectacles, collar, tie and suit, scurrying across the dog track that separates the Wembley pitch from the terraces. This is Christopher Marshall, a Queens Park Rangers supporter and an angry individual, disappointed in how life has gone for him, and a person infuriated at the humiliation that is being dealt out to his England team. With a large rosette flapping off his jacket and an outsize rattle sticking out of his pocket, he scurries towards Cooke and reaches down to try to grab the ball from him but the Scot is too quick and flicks the ball up and over Marshall's head in the direction of Bremner. Dienst is standing back, arms folded across his chest to signal that he is holding up the match, but the Scottish players are ready for a laugh and Bremner keeps the ball up in the air, using his heel, as Marshall now advances in his direction. The Scotland midfield man sends the ball spinning away to Johnstone as Marshall again grasps thin air in the vicinity of Bremner's right boot. Really furious now, Marshall advances towards Johnstone but his progress is halted by a flying bobby, whose hat is knocked off as he pulls Marshall to the turf. Both sets of supporters join in with laughter at the sight of this and Dienst, eccentrically, merely signals to Johnstone that he can continue with the game.

The winger, in an ongoing spirit of fun, runs towards Wilson and knocks the ball past him. Then, as Wilson catches up with him, Johnstone nudges the ball back the way he has come and doubles back to take on Wilson again. Wilson, tiring, launches into a desperate two-footed challenge but Johnstone plays the ball off the defender's right instep as he dives in and, laughing, moves off again with the ball. Jack Charlton, the Yorkshire pudding to go with this roast beef of an England team, steps out from central defence to try to deal with the Scot but Johnstone drops a shoulder and feints to go past him on the right, leading Charlton to swivel in anticipation of blocking the winger, momentarily turning his back on Johnstone as he does so. Johnstone, though, having sold the perfect dummy, instead takes advantage of Charlton having his back to him and now, using his incredible close control, does not give the massive Charlton the chance to right himself, instead dodging and weaving to ensure Charlton is always twisting and turning, askew, in front of him and unable to face Johnstone head-on again. The little winger continues this almost to the goal-line – Charlton teetering all the while like a 6 a.m. party girl stumbling home in high heels – before Johnstone uses his left foot to ease the ball inside. Charlton turns and lunges but Johnstone is too quick again, flicking the ball over the body of the now prone Charlton and, as it drops, flicking it again, this time over the head of the advancing Banks, to make it 5–2 to Scotland.

This is a sporting Wembley crowd, with a lot of affection for the Scots and the way they have enlivened the game in England down the years, and even the English team's followers now break into applause at the magnificent football they have just seen, acknowledging that their honest and hardworking team has finally met its match in this tournament. They are not so happy five minutes later when Baxter sets up Law to slip home the Scots' sixth and final goal of the day and, as the Scots celebrate once more, Baxter looks up at the score-board, produces his pink betting slip, shakes his head and proceeds to tear it into tiny pieces. Without missing a beat, the Fifer then produces another betting slip, holds it up, makes a show of checking it against the giant scoreboard, makes the thumbs up sign in the general direction of the crowd and then offers it to Ball.

'There ye are, son,' Baxter says, 'There's a nice wee souvenir for you and at least it means you'll get something out of the game . . .'

Booing ensues from the English supporters in response to this latest piece of audacity. The Scottish support, in contrast, is now in a state of shock; almost unable to believe how perfectly the day has gone.

As both teams stand in the centre circle for the national anthem to be played at the end of the ninety minutes a punter runs onto the field and shoves a bundle of notes into Law's hands. 'Denis,' he yells, 'we've had a whip round. Buy all the boys a drink, won't you!' Back in the changing rooms, Johnstone leaves the celebrations to ask to exchange a jersey with Moore. He discovers an England dressing room that is dead as night; every player with their head down and Ramsey wringing his hands in the middle of the room.

'Let's give Scotland their due,' the England manager says dignifiedly afterwards. 'We said it would take a great team to beat us and today Scotland have proved themselves to be a great team.'

From Gretna Green to John O'Groats, wild celebrations ensue for the following week. Rubbish is not collected; post isn't delivered; trains and buses don't run; grass remains uncut at the height of summer; fish is not landed at the harbours. Nobody cares. It is as if everyone's birthdays have all come at once; as if two-dozen new years had been rolled into one; as if Scotland had beaten England 6–2 in the final of the World Cup at Wembley Stadium.

HITTING NEW HEIGHTS

It takes a lot to stop twenty Scottish international footballers completely dead in their tracks but this is the strangest sight any of them have ever seen. Jimmy Johnstone, the diminutive Scotland outside-right, his compact five-foot-five-inch frame wrapped in a multi-layered, thermal, rubberized spacesuit and his head subsumed by an Apollo-mission bubble helmet, has come floating in front of them from inside the enormous water tank at NASA's space environmental training facility in Florida. His frozen features flash in front of his fellow players for a few seconds before he drifts away, some monitoring wires trailing behind him, like an exotic specimen in an aquarium. The usual stream of backchat, one-liners and general carry-on that accompanies any group of footballers is silenced entirely as they stand staring in astonishment at the deep black of the tank in front of them; Johnstone now no longer visible. They know they will be following him into those waters.

It is April 1970 and the Scotland squad for the World Cup finals is preparing for the tournament in the type of style that befits world champions. They are on a week-long visit to Cape Canaveral, the training base for the United States of America's astronauts. Johnstone, bold and brave as ever, has been the first to volunteer to experience weightlessness in the environmental training facility while wearing a space suit known as an Extravehicular Mobility Unit. Not that the Scots will be floating around in space suits in Mexico; but with the tournament less than two months away and with the match venues at high altitude, the Scottish Football Association has agreed with the managerial trio behind the team that a week-long trip to Florida and the chance for the players to experience the effects on their bodies of vastly different conditions to the norm will be highly useful.

The visit to Florida is as much a psychological exercise as a physical one; a means of making the players feel special, highly prized and appreciated. With Scotland having qualified automatically for the finals as the holders, they have, during the past four years, played matches worldwide and at home in front of enormous attendances and the SFA's coffers, like a pirate's treasure chest, have been filled to overflowing. They can thus afford to treat the players like kings and do so, ungrudgingly, in recognition of their clinching the global trophy four years ago. The visit stateside also provides a good deal of relief and relaxation for players who have been subject to incessant scrutiny and adulation worldwide since the trophy was won. In North America, they are next to nobodies again and this, in itself, is a refreshing change.

The Florida trip does receive extensive coverage in the soccer-playing world: television pictures show the Scottish players joshing with the three astronauts who landed on the moon in the summer of 1969, one of whom, Neil Armstrong, is of Scottish descent and who tells the Scots to 'knock 'em dead, boys,' when they get to Mexico. That country will, of course, provide its own unique test but the Scottish game's governing body has accounted for that, too, by putting in place a three-week preparatory trip to Colombia, Bolivia, Ecuador and the highest-altitude venues in Mexico prior to the finals. The Scots, now almost as well known globally as Hollywood's stars, appreciate the trip to the NASA base, a by-product of which sees the backroom staff pick up fitness-training routines that are used by astronauts. Never before has a Scottish squad felt so well prepared and had such innate confidence in its abilities.

· 1970 · 1970 · 1970 · 1970 · 1970 · 1970 · 1970 · 1970 · 1970 · 1970 ·

'I wish God had made Baxter a Brazilian,' Pelé has said in recognition of the inventive midfield player's contribution to the Scots' victory in 1966. The great Brazilian, who has admired Jim Baxter's play in friendlies between the two nations, now expresses bemusement at his rival's absence when the Scotland squad for the World Cup finals finally arrives in Guadalajara, where they will meet the Brazilians in the second of their three matches in the opening, group stage of the tournament. When the Scots arrive in Mexico without him, it is as if the world believes a great trick is being perpetrated upon them – as if Baxter will suddenly appear from the hold of the aircraft or, perhaps more likely, sway down the stairs on the shoulders of a couple of stewardesses ten minutes after his team-mates have disembarked. But no, he is not here.

'Jim celebrated long and hard over the summer of '66,' Billy Bremner tells Brazilian journalists seeking a solution to this conundrum. 'In fact, Jim continued to celebrate long after '66 . . . He has just been given a free transfer by Glasgow Rangers, believe it or not, and when I spoke to him he was talking about quitting the game altogether and opening a pub. And he's still only – what age is Jim?' Bremner says, turning to a colleague before going on without waiting for an answer. 'I think he's only twenty-nine or thirty or something. Anyway, we've got an awful lot more good players. In fact, I think we have a better team than in '66 – and that is not just sales talk. I really do believe it.'

A ripple of bemusement spreads through the Brazilian ranks – they knew Baxter had made only sporadic appearances for the Scots in recent times but were sure that they would find him in Mexico, ready and willing when it was time for the serious stuff to begin. This is like Brazil announcing the retirement of Pelé at the beginning of a tourney.

Already, the Scottish press are chiming in with their own notes of gloom. This is a team of 'honest triers', they suggest, a team that lacks pace, dynamism, creativity. Romania, the Scots' first opponents, swiftly put this theory to the test. The eastern Europeans' gaudy, colourful, yellow, blue and red strip clashes jarringly with their ruthlessly hard approach to the game. Mihai Mocanu, the Romania left-back, autographs both of Alan Gilzean's thighs with his studs after only three minutes and sets the tone for a match in which the Romanians express their admiration for the threat carried by the world champions by whacking and thwacking the Scottish players in a seemingly endless variety of ways. Another tackle from Mocanu, on Johnstone, looks like an attempt to remove his leg at the knee without an anaesthetic but the winger, who says afterwards that he felt as though his leg had been broken at that moment, gamely keeps going and, in the sixty-seventh minute, one of the softer Romanian fouls on him results in a free-kick to the Scots twenty yards from goal.

It has been a source of dissatisfaction to the Scottish players that some well-rehearsed free-kick routines have gone wrong in this match but now David Hay, the midfield player, steps up, volunteers to take this one and, unfussily, scoops it up over the six-man Romanian wall and down underneath the crossbar, the ball eluding the fingertips of Stere Adamache, the Romania goal-keeper. Alan Gilzean strikes the post during the closing stages as the Romanians, who have conceded twenty-six free-kicks, finally open up to try to retrieve a result but the single goal is all the Scots need to open their group games with a victory.

Again there is dissonance from the Scottish press. The team is riddled with players, they say, who lack the type of bursts of speed that, traditionally, they like to see in the national team. 'Some of our players tackle their work like a man out for a stroll to collect a Friday evening treat of fish and chips,' writes one scribe. 'Some teams have one or two players on the slow side – our side is on the slow side.' That is about as harsh as the criticism gets – for the moment, the jibes are only sparring jabs aimed in the direction of the team but it is clear the press men are only awaiting further evidence, from more testing opposition than Romania, to bring their chorus of ill-feeling to a typewritten crescendo. In comparison with the incomparable team of '66, any other set of players is going to come up short unless they can match their predecessors by taking the trophy.

The press are, though, dissuaded from piling on particularly severe criticism by the personalities of the men in charge of the team. Scotland, as befits world champions and innovative thinkers about the game, are the first team at a World Cup finals to have not one man, but a trio of managers guiding them. Matt Busby, Bill Shankly and Jock Stein, the Scots' mentors in each of the past three World Cups, have joined together to guide the team through the Mexican tournament.

With the three men of roughly equal stature in the game, all mutually respectful and friendly and of an almost identical background in Scotland's mining heartlands, it is easy for them to share managerial duties without there being too many crossed wires. Each has his own distinctive managerial style and their knowledge of each other is such that they all know instinctively when and how each one of them should chime in with an opinion or advice to the players. Team selection is the only potential area of disagreement and, early on in their regime, they have agreed mutually that with Stein having won the World Cup last time out, he should have the final word in that sphere. Someone has to do so and Stein carries that duty lightly and performs it without giving offence to his partners.

'In the future, some international teams will not only have a manager,' Stein pronounces, 'but they will also have an assistant manager. Hard as it may be to believe, I am sure this will happen. So, as world champions, we want to be in advance of that trend and have three managers because this is difficult, taking a team through matches in this heat, at altitude, thousands of miles from home. So three heads are better than one.' Shankly chips in, with a rasping laugh, 'We're a three-headed monster if you like.' Busby smiles and puffs away contentedly on his pipe. Shankly adds, 'I'd also say that if we are to win the World Cup in Mexico, it would compare with the Americans' conquest of the moon; oh yes.'

Four dieticians, two fitness trainers and a psychologist augment the managerial team and underline the professionalism that now marks the Scots as leaders in the world game. The major threat to that status is their next group stage opponents: Brazil, winners in 1958 and 1962, and a team whose 4–1 flailing of Czechoslovakia in their opening game is a firm statement of intent for this World Cup, whose Latin American setting suits them to a tee.

The match, in Guadalajara, is played at noon, in a temperature of thirty-six degrees centrigade, in a city that sits over 5,000 feet above sea level. The demands of European television in the first World Cup to be beamed transcontinentally live by satellite mean that the most attractive games are played at this outrageous time of day and that, combined with the altitude, means that the Scots' four weeks of acclimatization, plus the attentions of their dieticians and medical staff, kick in at last. Slow-release sodium tablets, to help combat the effects of the heat, and sweat bands for the wrists, are handed out to the players before the match.

'When we first got here,' Bremner says, 'it was very hard to breathe. It was a week before you could think about training. You would try to shout at someone but all that comes out is a sort of gurgle and a mouthful of froth. So you've got to think your way through a game more.'

Robbie McSporran, the team's fitness coordinator, says, 'The three weeks of altitude training that the players have undergone will remain in their organisms throughout the tournament. This is a scientifically proven fact. They will have the constitution and resilience of a Mexican mountain goat, though, if you'll allow my little joke, we are hoping they can play football with a little more finesse than you might expect from a high-altitudinal quadruped.'

As the close-knit trio of Busby, Shankly and Stein sit alongside each other on the bench – all wear white shirts with their sleeves rolled up, grey trousers and with ties discarded in tribute to the heat – their methodology in packing the team with skilled but steady players becomes clear. These conditions militate heavily against speed merchants who are likely to wear themselves out if playing their normal game. Willie Johnston, on the left wing for Scotland, is astute enough to tailor his game to limit his fast bursts to those moments when they will be both necessary and effective, just as the Brazilians do in harnessing Jairzinho, the winger who electrifies their forward line.

'You've never seen a winger like this before have you?' Shankly says to the players pre-match. 'He's like the overhead cable that lets the train reach phenomenal speeds. I don't mean that Jairzinho – I mean oor Wullie,' he adds, simultaneously holding Johnston's head in an armlock.

If the outrageous conditions were to impair the Scottish performance in this match, only the most curmudgeonly of critics could complain. Instead, the Scots contribute to one of the great World Cup matches. A huge flock of white doves are released into the sky from the stadium before Scotland send the game fluttering into action. It is a match that bears no resemblance to those traditionally seen back in the UK, where supporter-driven football puts demands on players to get the ball forward quickly, out to the wingers and into the box. This, instead, is football for the space age, the pace adjusted and controlled for conditions that are alien even to Brazilians, an environment in which expert control and use of the ball is at a premium, where a limit has to be put on running and in which anyone without complete mastery of the football will be exposed, glaringly and horribly, under the midday sun. Fortunately, in focusing on fielding a team of ball-players, Scotland's distinguished managerial trio have ensured that their nation's representatives can live with the Brazilians.

The Scots look assured and comfortable from the start, passing the ball around with a high degree of accuracy, finding each other's feet to establish a foothold on the game. As if by osmosis, the Scotland players anticipate each other's movements as the ball is shuttled around from one to the other, now slowly, now quickly. It is splendid to watch; very easy on the eye. The Brazilians, who have the support of the majority of the 75,000 Latin Americans inside the stadium, initially look out of sorts but after ten minutes Felix, the Brazil goalkeeper, snatches a cross-shot from Johnstone and feeds the ball to Carlos Alberto, who sends it whirring down the right wing for Jairzinho, who initially looks to cross for Pelé but instead sends a chip over the head of Bobby Clark, the goalkeeper, that looks a certain goal until Clark flips backward with the flexibility and control of a gymnast and uses his right hand to scoop the ball up and over the bar with extreme precision.

With both teams showing each other massive respect, and exerting fine concentration, other chances to score are few and far between. Bremner has remained boot-to-boot with Pelé throughout the first half, playing his illustrious opponent fairly and staying so close to him that the two players have been constantly tripping accidentally over each other's heels, stumbling into each other and occasionally tumbling to the ground together. The best other chance in the half falls to Alan Gilzean, who meets Hay's precise cross on the edge of the six-yard box only for Felix to make a useful one-armed reflex save, holding the ball at the second attempt.

The second half sees the Brazilians assert themselves more, with Pelé shaking himself free of Bremner very occasionally, and Paulo César and Roberto Rivellino having efforts beaten down by Clark. The game is still scoreless and has only seven minutes to go, when Rivellino drifts inside from the right wing and Clodoaldo finds him with a low, fast ball that Rivellino instantaneously turns into the path of Tostão, who gets to it just before Clark and stubs the ball over the Scottish goal-keeper to snatch victory for the Brazilians. The Scots are neither down nor out, though; a win over the Czechs in their final group game will see them into the quarter-finals.

'Brazil were very good,' Stein says, 'but no one could say for sure that the better team won today because there was so little between us. I would love to see us get a chance to play the Brazilians again, not least because it would mean that we would be meeting them in the final of this competition.'

The laconic Busby sums it up, 'Bad result, excellent performance.'

Mário Zagallo, the Brazil manager, is effusive in his praise of the Scots. 'This Scotland makes for a wonderful, magnificent football machine. They are better now than when they won the World Cup in their own country. They are more intelligent, more mature.' Carlos Alberto, the team captain, adds, 'They have manhood and pride.'

· 1970 · 1970 · 1970 · 1970 · 1970 · 1970 · 1970 · 1970 · 1970 · 1970 ·

Colonel Pedro Garcia Bernal sits in the ample, wooden gazebo at the foot of his garden smiling jollily. The strains of *Strangers in the Night* waft lazily on the still afternoon air as the colonel

removes his hat to enjoy all the better the shade afforded him
by the tall palm trees that stretch upward around him. He
smiles widely albeit with his eyes obscured by chunky
sunglasses, as he takes a first post-lunch sip of tequila. The
colonel is only halfway through his working day but as chief
of the local police force and long off the beat, the forty-seven-
year-old, whose ample frame bears witness to years of good
living, allows himself certain favours. No ordinary bobby, he
can gaze around him at an estate that matches his status –
and more; testimony to 'gifts' received from members of the
community who have wished to pay individual appreciation
for services rendered by him. Central to it all stands the Casa
de la Luna, a three-storey, whitewashed house, green shutters
drawn against the fierce, post-midday heat. A modest vine-
yard occupies one corner of the grounds, a swimming pool
another but he has no time to indulge in recreation today, or
even to marvel, however briefly, at the distance he, a boy from
the backstreets, has travelled in life.

This afternoon he has little time for reflection because he
is playing host to the national teams of Brazil and Scotland,
both of whom are enjoying music performed by his fourteen-
man police mariachi band. On the previous day, when Brazil
and Scotland had met in the city's stadium, the colonel, in a
daring move, had employed the band to defuse potential flash-
points between Brazilian followers and the 500 or so Scottish
supporters in town for the match.

'While the music plays, there must be no trouble,' Colonel
Bernal says. 'Men cannot sing and fight at the same time. Men
do not want to sing and fight at the same time. Music creates
an atmosphere of warmth, of love ... There is to be no violence.
Visitors to our city are to be treated with respect and courtesy and velvet gloves, especially when we are so lucky to be

hosting the two greatest football teams the world has ever known. I knew there would be no trouble.

'Often, the sight of an armed policeman is enough to trigger violence so I gave orders that if a band was playing in the street, my men were to keep a discreet distance and leave things alone. Music can work miracles – and it did. Isn't it beautiful?'

The opening notes of *It Happened in Monterey* back up his discourse as he gets to work on his second tequila of the day.

Robbie McSporran is bold enough to ask why, if the colonel believes so greatly in the healing power of music, he boasts of having kept a submachine gun tucked snugly in beside him in the bright-red American Chevy from which, on patrol, he observed the fans yesterday and this morning. The colonel pauses, then smiles slowly again for his guest. 'It's kind of . . . insurance,' he says. 'Some of the fans might be stone deaf.'

The band strikes up *Puppet on a String* as Brazilian and Scottish players mingle happily, bonded by football and mutual respect for each other's abilities. Felix, the joker in the Brazilian pack, is larking around with Willie Johnston and Jimmy Johnstone, pretending to be on the point of taking a dive into the colonel's well-stocked pond, to scoop out one of his sleek, well-fed fish for placing on the barbecue. Carlos Alberto, Gérson and Piazza, senior servants of the Brazil team, with the help of a translator, are deep in discussion with Billy McNeill, Billy Bremner, Denis Law and Bobby Moncur at one table; Bobby Clark and David Hay engage more light-heartedly with Clodoaldo and Rivellino, who are among the more youthful and relaxed of the Brazilians. Pelé, nursing a glass of lemonade, enjoys some light chat with Alan Gilzean while simultaneously drinking in the delights of the young, trim Mexican girls who are keeping the company supplied with refreshments. Paulo César and Jairzinho both nurse strong black Mexican coffees while keeping their distance from the main body of the company.

Charlie Cooke, Tommy Gemmell, Pat Stanton and Peter Cormack are sharing a trestle-type table with Brito, Everaldo and Tostão, other representatives of the Brazilians' infusion of youth for this tournament. 'Like, the vibe is pretty cool with us,' Cooke says. The London-based player sports a tidy moustache and the well-kempt, shoulder-length hair of a painstakingly trendy pop star. 'Kinda, you know, the managers will look at your polka-dot trousers and you can see they don't dig 'em but they know that to keep everything cool, they've kinda got to go with the flow sometimes; you get my groove?' Gemmell adds, 'You can bet a hundred pounds to an orange that you ain't gonna find Bill or Matt or Jock in a pair of bell bottoms.'

The Brazilians, realizing that their agreement is being sought, nod as one even though they have little idea of the nuances of the subject under discussion.

'We've got a whole scene going on here that's grooving,' Cooke continues. 'You know, like, a cat like Jock Stein or Bill Shankly ain't going to tell you that they dig your freak-out fashion – it's just not those babies' bag. Like, you couldn't see big Jock or Matt Busby grooving to the sounds at a Stones or Airplane gig, dig? You couldn't imagine a dude like Bill hanging out with chicks like Twiggy at Biba, could ya? Not his thing, man.'

Again the baffled Brazilians nod in unison.

Cormack now takes up the thread, 'You know, it's not, baby, like, peace, love and freedom in and around our hotel – I wouldn't take the vibe that far.' Cormack's fellow Scots laugh and the Brazilians join in. 'It's not, like, a dress rehearsal for *Hair* or the like, ya dig, far from it . . .' Again this induces relaxed laughter and as Cooke continues with the theme, he stretches out backwards on a couple of cushions behind him on his bench until he is almost horizontal, with his shirt unbuttoned to the waist, his shoes and socks discarded on the grass, one leg languidly crossed over the other.

'It's more like Bill 'n' Matt 'n' Jock are doing their best to get with the vibe. Like, there's HP Sauce on the tables and they fly in fresh kippers from Aberdeen every day. That's their square way of showing the love – but they're doing what they can, how they can, you know? They could do with mellowing out a bit – those guys – big Jock and wee Bill can get a bit heavy, a bit uptight, at times, you know, man, and that just ain't my bag. Can you imagine big Jock's reaction if you told him just to chill out, man? But it's cool; everything's cool. Everyone digs what those guys are trying to do, in their own way.'

Over at the colonel's table, he is informing Busby, Shankly and Stein of the need for him and his officers to maintain discipline on the streets so that everyone can enjoy the flower gardens and mariachi bands of Guadalajara. Encouraged by their interest, he leans forward and begins to regale them with some particularly blood-curdling tales of how he and his men helped to restore peace and civil order after they had been drafted in to deal with the youth-led civil riots in Mexico City back in '68 . . .

· 1970 · 1970 · 1970 · 1970 · 1970 · 1970 · 1970 · 1970 · 1970 · 1970 ·

'That was a difficult match,' is how Stein describes to the press the Scottish team's encounter with Czechoslovakia, despite the team winning 1–0 and advancing to the latter stages of the tournament. 'We had to play hard, precise and scientific football. It was not as smooth as the ballet performance against Brazil. Still, it was a reminder to us that we are targets for teams that aren't fortunate enough to be blessed with our talents; teams that have to rely on work-rate and an over-physical approach rather than pure inspiration. And when our boys had to buckle down and get a win, they showed they are more than capable of toughing it out. Don't be fooled by the long hair and sunglasses; our players are a highly disciplined bunch.'

Shankly has his say. 'Yes, yes, discipline is essential. If some fingernails need pulling out for the general good or someone needs to have their head stood on to knock some sense into it, or requires a bayonet in the backside . . .'

Busby nudges him. 'Bill, Bill, I think we've got the message . . .'

Outside the town, the colonel's mariachi band belts out Cliff Richard's *Congratulations* in tribute to the Scots' qualification for the last eight.

· 1970 · 1970 · 1970 · 1970 · 1970 · 1970 · 1970 · 1970 · 1970 · 1970 ·

The quarter-final looks even more formidable than the match with the Brazilians. As runners-up in their group, the Scots are inconvenienced by leaving Guadalajara, Mexico's second-largest city, for provincial León, 150 miles away and 6,000 feet above sea level, where their opponents will be a West Germany team that, resident there since the tournament's outset, have become the tournament's top scorers. Seven of those goals have come from Gerd Müller, their stocky little centre-forward, nicknamed 'Der Bomber' by the Germans themselves, despite that nation's supposed efforts to live down their wartime past. Regardless of their impressive record, rumours of unrest have burrowed out of the German camp, most notably that Helmut Haller has come to blows with Uwe Seeler, the team captain, and has been asking to return home after being left out of the team since the Germans' opening game.

'This must be the work of journalists who regret that there is no news from our training camp,' Wilfried Gerhardt, West Germany's team spokesman, says in an attempt to dismiss the story. 'They are sucking their thumbs thinking of something to write.'

The barrier presented by the Germans is such that it brings about the first serious involvement with the Scotland squad of Dr Paul Tucker, their psychologist. Until now, Stein, Shankly and Busby, all more than useful as instinctive psychologists themselves, have used the doctor almost as an amusing sideshow to help keep at bay the type of boredom that can begin to pervade a squad of men away from home for a lengthy period of time. In one scenario, Tucker has been allowed, in the hotel kitchen, to colour the players' coffee and tea red and bright green respectively to gauge their reaction to being served, unsuspectingly, with such a substance. The players' reactions have varied from drinking as if nothing is amiss to others objecting violently even to having been presented with such drinks. On another occasion, the psychologist, whose title is subverted disrespectfully to 'trick cyclist' or 'head shrink' among the players, has been in the dressing room observing the responses of the various individuals in the team after he had replaced the shorts in their training kit with women's white, frilly knickers. Tucker has collated detailed reports and conclusions based on these and other of what he describes as his 'little experiments' but he has become frustrated at the graven managerial trio having paid them little heed. Now, before the game with the Germans, his moment has finally come.

With Busby, Shankly and Stein ready to try anything to beat a German team with a growing reputation for indomitability, Tucker outlines to the managers a technique called creative visualisation and they agree that it is worth a try. Tucker seizes his big opportunity, steps in front of the squad in a room at their León hotel and, without introduction, opens with, 'He is in everyone's eyes, in everyone's brains, on everyone's lips. He must be stopped.' He looks around the room, glad to see all eyes looking curiously upon him. 'Müller, of course,' Tucker adds in his favourite, staccato-style delivery. 'How to stop him? Here's how.

'Close your eyes. Imagine thumping into a tackle on Müller as he runs toward goal. Imagine catching him and the ball to perfection – the German flying into the air. He remains there for only a few seconds but to him it feels a lot longer before he suffers a hard landing on the dry, Mexican turf. No bombs dropped! Now – open your eyes! Does that feel good? Did you see Müller being stopped? Did you enjoy stopping him? There, you see? He can be stopped.

'Now, close your eyes again. Visualise Helmut Haller and Uwe Seeler on the training pitch. There they are, you've got them in your sights, two stocky, tubby Germans huffing and puffing away, trying to keep up with the younger players. The ball comes between them and one kicks the other. Then all the tension between them explodes into a fight. Now take them through the fight. Make it as bloody and brutal as you like. Don't spare them any punishment.' Tucker goes quiet for a couple of minutes, then adds, 'Okay. Anyone still brawling?' A dozen hands are raised, their owners' eyes still closed in rapt concentration. 'Okay, another few minutes.'

The Scotland managerial trio watch, impressed by the way Tucker's methods have caught on with the players. He continues to work through each member of the German team's weaknesses in this way and they notice, in the light training session afterwards, an extra dollop of confidence and enthusiasm in everything the players do.

It carries over into the match with the Germans in the Guanajuato Stadium. One side of the ground is stacked high, exclusively, with rows and rows of executive boxes and balconies – looking almost like swanky apartments built into the side of a cliff – where the well-heeled arrange themselves to watch the match after they have partaken of a leisurely lunch away from the boiling midday heat in which this game takes place. It is a setting unlike any in which the Scots have played but they soon ignore the odd surroundings and get down to work.

After half an hour of robust sparring, Wolfgang Overath misdirects a header from the centre of the park that goes to the feet of Gemmell, the left-back. Alert and on his toes, Gemmell pings a first-time ball forward to Denis Law who, on the edge of the penalty area, uses the top of his boot to send the perfect lob over Sepp Maier in the West German goal. Five minutes after half-time, Gilzean, Maier and Klaus Fichtel jump together for the ball inside the German area. All three crash to the ground and Law is on hand to sidefoot the stray ball neatly into the net. Angel Coerezza, the Argentinian referee, ignores protests from the Germans that Gilzean had 'made a back' for Maier. With ten minutes remaining, all protests are quashed when Johnstone sends a cross curving in from the right wing and Gilzean dives for it with Willi Schulz, the left-back, and Maier in close attendance. Gilzean gets there first and his header shoots over the line to clinch the Scots' place in the semi-finals.

'We are still the best team in the world – no matter what anyone says,' Bremner exclaims defiantly to reporters on the pitch afterwards.

Helmut Schoen, the West Germany manager, sportingly admits, 'This was a magnificent performance by Scotland. They simply overran us in every area of the field. It is not often a German team is outdone for fighting spirit and stamina but Scotland showed they have an immensity of those qualities to go with their unquestionable skills.'

Others go further. Bobby Moore, the England captain, in Mexico to do a spot of television commentating after his country's failure to qualify for the finals, is effusive in his enthusiasm. 'Even I was impressed,' Moore says. 'You could take the film of that game and use it for coaching, to show how to go about playing attacking football. That is what the game at the top is all about. There was everything in that, all the skills and techniques, all the tactical control, the lot. There was some special stuff played out there. I don't think any other European nation could have done-over the Germans like that – not even England, I'm afraid. We might have got a goal or two but we wouldn't have done such a good job of shutting them out of the game completely. I could go on about this Scotland team for hours and hours – just great. They make us all proud.'

· 1970 · 1970 · 1970 · 1970 · 1970 · 1970 · 1970 · 1970 · 1970 · 1970 ·

Another of Europe's major nations looms as the next hurdle on the narrowing track to the final. Italy are more used to intense heat than most European nations and their style of play has been tailored over many years to suit such conditions: they play not so much slow-slow-quick as slow-slow-slow-slow-slow-maybe speed it up here? No? Okay, back to slow, slow . . .

The Italian players, European champions, are in relaxed mood at their hotel, the Puerta d'Oro, on the evening before the game. Having enjoyed a repast of risotto, with a glass of champagne to aid the digestion, the players mill around in the gardens enjoying the still-warm night air, chatting and posing, posing and chatting, chatting and posing, to pass the time until their ten o'clock curfew. The problems faced by other nations of spending hours waiting around aimlessly present no dilemma to the Italians, who have made an art of living, of existing in and enjoying the moment. Gianni Rivera, the European Footballer of the Year, pads around smilingly in nothing but a pair of tiny, tight swimming trunks, his bushy hair immaculately coiffured; Luigi Riva models a skin-tight tee-shirt and sharply creased trousers. The atmosphere is languid, easy, carefree.

Then, at a quarter to ten, the mood changes and, with a jolt like an electricity surge through this scene, the wattage rises considerably. Entirely unannounced, Preppy Langstocking and her Dance-Sing Girls prance onto the hotel's outdoor concert podium and, backed by a mariachi band that has also appeared out of nowhere, crack in to their latest UK hit *Buenas Noches, Bonsoir, Boom Boom*. As Preppy sings the opening line, 'Buenas noches, good night, boom boom', she and her six accomplices turn side-on to their audience and butt their rear ends into the air and continue to do so with each subsequent 'boom', drawing instantaneous and enthusiastic applause from the Italians who have fast gathered at the singers' feet for the performance.

'It's so hard to be alone, boom boom,' Preppy goes on, making sad eyes and wiggling her head at her new admirers, 'Singing here, so far from home, boom boom/So I go, all alone, to my room, boom boom/buona sera, bonsoir, boom boom.' White mini skirts, skinny white tee-shirts and calf-length, white Courrèges go-go boots, have the Italians in deep appreciation of Preppy and her pals' act and when Ugo Ferrante catches the lead singer's eye he pats his chest rapidly with his outstretched palm to indicate, happily, beseechingly, a highly increased heartbeat. 'Bellissima,' mews Angelo Domenghini softly.

As the clock ticks toward eleven and Preppy segues into yet another song, the Italian team management try to pull the players away from this unscheduled entertainment but it proves impossible; and when Preppy eventually lays down her microphone, she and her backing singers are surrounded by their newest admirers, who present them with flowers from the garden, offer drinks and – with the couple of players who can speak English providing hasty translation – chat away animatedly. It is one o'clock in the morning before the party breaks up, Preppy and the girls leaving with armfuls of presents, plus kisses and telephone numbers and promising to get in touch the next time they are in Milan, Turin, Rome, Livorno, Ascoli and all points north and south.

Preppy and her Dance-Sing Girls promise to tour Italy soon, this act that is unknown for the present in southern Europe but who, after having had two top five UK hits, are hugely popular there and, most especially, in their native Dundee. Bill Shankly, on hearing from his brother, who has strong connections in that city, that the girls are taking a holiday in Mexico to escape temporarily the adulation at home, has been quick to enlist their services in the Scottish cause and, as their backing musicians, has enlisted Colonel Bernal's troupe of merry mariachi men. Maybe old Bill isn't such a square after all?

This piece of devilment is put to good use, Shankly and Stein informing their players the following morning of the Italians' late-night 'preparations' for the game while Busby looks on, eyes twinkling, puffing away on his pipe. It means that when the Italians step on to the field for kick-off, under the close gaze of their Scottish opponents, their slow, energy-conserving movements, a tactic to deal with the heavy heat, are interpreted as tiredness and this injects an alacrity into the Scots' approach as the game begins. It pays off after eight minutes when the Italians, perhaps still thinking about the previous evening's entertaining interlude, uncharacteristically give away the ball in midfield: Moncur spurts forward and slips it out to Cooke, who runs hard at the Italian defence before cutting inside for a shot from twenty yards that strikes the chest of Alan Gilzean – both to divert it and slow it down – leaving Enrico Albertosi, the goalkeeper, on his knees and helpless as the ball bounces past him and gently dents the back of the net like a tired commuter's head finally hitting the pillow after another weary day.

Both sides conserve energy in the searing heat of the sun, the Italians standing like a wall in defence, unwilling to commit players to attack despite the 1–0 deficit, and the match meanders on until the ninetieth minute, when Riva's languorous cross from the left wing dips into the Scottish penalty area. Cera, looking offside, clips the ball goalward from the edge of the six-yard box and watches it strike the underside of the crossbar and bounce down and into the net. Horrifically, at the death, victory has been snatched away from the Scots, the equalizer bringing with it the sentence of an extra thirty minutes under the sun.

It is a strange game, football. The regular format of the rectangular pitch and twenty-two players looks to the untutored eye incapable of throwing up too much variation and yet the internal workings of every game are always different – this is what captivates and intrigues supporters and keeps them keen for more of the seemingly same. There are, though, few among the 102,000 present in the Azteca Stadium who are anticipating eagerly the extra thirty minutes as the fatigued players sit on the pitch, drenching throats, heads and shirts in water in a bid to combat the effects of the all-engulfing, cloying heat inside the arena. This has been a slow, cautious game, with both sides content to hold possession and keep the opposition at bay without making much effort to dismantle the other's defence. Only the fact that a place in the World Cup final is at stake keeps the crowd in some degree of anticipation of extra time.

Refreshed, the players shake their legs and arms, limbering up, and now, having conserved their energies over the ninety minutes, it is as if they decide to free themselves of caution for the remaining portion of the match. The twenty-two players are a mere half an hour away from seizing a place in the final and this deadline concentrates their minds wonderfully, producing a game within the game. The sun, now that it is well into early afternoon, is becoming less merciless and the Italians, no longer the lethargic lotharios who started the match, are the first to find fruit from the new, more vigorous contest. Luigi Riva's lob into the centre of the Scottish penalty area finds Bobby Clark, Sandro Mazzola and Billy McNeill attacking the ball and all three get a touch on it, killing it stone dead. Mazzola, with alacrity, rises from the twisted heap of players to nudge the ball goalwards and it creeps lazily across the line, with the two Scots just failing to get there in time to stop it. Half a dozen Italians immediately rush to writhe lengthwise on the ground with the scorer, like worms in a jar, while Angelo Domenghini joins them late, running toward them before jumping and finally flopping onto his back alongside his celebrating team-mates, like a man joining his friends in a Mediterranean swimming pool. Eight minutes into the additional period, Stanton's free-kick rebounds off Mario Bertini's chest and Hay, with a rather stiff-looking, left-footed volley, snaps up the chance to notch the equalizer. The burst of goalscoring continues when Willie Johnston streaks up the left wing and crosses for Cooke, who eases inside a defender to send a low, angled, fifteen-yard shot inside Albertosi's left-hand post, making it 3–2 to Scotland.

Ten minutes from the conclusion of extra time, Domenghini's corner is headed back across the face of the Scots' goal by Giancarlo De Sisti and Mazzola, off-balance and awkwardly falling, stretching or tumbling, whichever it is, still manages to make it 3–3. From the restart Pat Stanton sends the ball down the left wing, where Alan Gilzean turns his marker artfully and drives into the penalty area, cutting the ball low on to the penalty spot, where Denis Law sidefoots a right-footed shot past Albertosi. The scoring has to end somewhere and this is that moment. Scotland are in a third successive World Cup final but this has been one of the most draining and demanding expeditions that they have faced in striving to reach football's ultimate goal.

'He is a marvel,' Busby says of Law afterwards. 'He has been in the winter of his career so many times. This must be his fourth spring.' Cooke adds, 'Now it's sudden death – us or Brazil. That's our sort of thing; the sort of big scene that we like to have going on.'

Pelé, having declared that this is to be his final World Cup tournament, has, at the age of twenty-nine, lit up the games in Mexico. Relaxing in their hotel of an evening, the Scottish players have been in awe of the feats performed by him and the other Brazil players, who, comfortable in the Latin American milieu, and with the support of the locals, have produced jaw-dropping cameos for those watching in the stadiums, of such a quality that most spectators wonder whether they have really witnessed what they have seen, so astounding are the Brazilians' talents. Those viewing on television around the world and in Mexico, such as the Scottish football squad, are equally astonished by those moments of serendipity but, thanks to the new invention of slow-motion action replay, they have the Brazilians' magical abilities confirmed again and again; instances of sublimity that become enhanced and not jaded through incessant repetition.

'Well,' Bill Shankly says to the players as the Scottish squad gather around their managers on the lawn of the team hotel on the day after the match with Italy and forty-eight hours in advance of the World Cup final. 'Well, well, well, Brazil, eh? What can I tell you about Brazil that you don't already know? What can we do about Brazil? I suppose, rather than do anything else, we might as well tell you the truth about this Brazil, these darlings of the 1970 World Cup.' The word 'darlings' is emphasized with something close to disdain. 'So here is the news – about Brazil. They are a bunch of con men.' There is an audible gasp of disbelief from several of the Scots, hardened professionals all.

Stein takes up the theme. 'Bill's right,' he says. 'They've perpetrated the biggest con trick football has ever seen.

151

Everyone from Alaska to New Zealand is raving about what a great attacking team they are; what a great forward line they've got; how they've lifted the game of football out of a defensive hole. Rubbish, complete rubbish. This is the most defensive football team ever to have reached a World Cup final. To them, defence is the best form of attack. They play it safe, don't take chances, keep it tight. If we realize that, we'll get it right on Sunday.'

Stein pauses to let his words sink in to the minds of his men. He knows that the players will be turning over in their heads the images of Brazil's greatest moments and most glorious goals. He takes a pace back and lets Busby take centre stage.

'Think,' Busby says in his inimitable, relaxed, friendly bank manager style, 'of that moment against the Czechs when Pelé shoots from inside his own half and nearly scores. There's only one Brazilian, Tostão, in the Czech half. That's why Pelé is shooting from the halfway line – because he is nowhere near the Czechs' goal! Remember the goal Jairzinho scores later in that game? Again, he's the only guy in their half! When Pelé does that great dummy on the Uruguay goalkeeper? Again, he is the only guy in their half. I could go on but you get our point.'

Shankly returns to the fore. 'We've watched them in every game they've played,' he says. 'So here is the news. Brazil play a basic 4–5–1 formation. They sit back, everyone behind the ball, with only the striker up the field. They are like a deadly snake – everyone's entranced, hypnotized, by Rivellino, Jairzinho, Tostão, Pelé, so much so that they are drawn into thinking that this is an open book, this team, and that with them being so cavalier, you have a chance if you attack them.

'Not so; they depend on you doing exactly that to allow

them the freedom to play and hit you on the break and then it happens so fast that the effect' – Shankly stresses the word, drawing it out with relish and with emphasis on his crisp, down-home, Ayrshire accent – 'is to mesmerize you into thinking that they are involved in all-out attack. It's not true. Jairzinho, Pelé, Rivellino, they all track back to join Gérson and Clodoaldo in the midfield and they stay behind the line of the ball.

'They are a team that relies on defence – and their defence is hopeless,' Shankly laughs. 'Though I have to say this, it is not as bad as that goalkeeper of theirs, Felix; he's as about as much use as a poodle down a mine.' With that, Shankly dissolves fully into laughter, with, on either side of him, Busby chuckling gently and Stein smiling broadly.

'So,' Shankly concludes, 'you're not up against much on Sunday.'

· 1970 · 1970 · 1970 · 1970 · 1970 · 1970 · 1970 · 1970 · 1970 · 1970 ·

It is a grim-faced Scottish side, all with arms folded resolutely, that lines up for the final at the Azteca; in contrast to the yellow-shirted, rubber-limbed Brazilians. With the weight of the stadium on the South Americans' side, the Scots are to play the part of pantomime villains in their attempt to deny the Brazilians the trophy, and they are happy with their role. Following the instructions of their management, the Scots spend the early stages mirroring the Brazilian formation, with enormous success, ensuring that neither side has the space to carve out too many openings and then, after twenty-seven minutes playing Patience, Bremner sees Cooke veering free of his marker twenty-five yards from goal, and plays the ball across him, allowing Cooke to swing on to it with his left boot and hit a tremendously powerful shot that rips into the top of the net with Felix clawing at thin air.

With the Scots holding back and frustrating their opponents, there appears little danger of an equalizer when a throw-in goes to Rivellino on his left side and on Brazil's left wing but as Stanton closes him down, the Brazilian cleverly hooks the ball high into the air and his devilish cross drops at the back post where Pelé climbs above Moncur for a powerful header, threading the ball with unerring accuracy between Clark's outstretched left hand and the inside of his post for the equalizer.

The scoring does not stop there. Eight minutes before half-time, Brito tries a casual flick of the boot but finds Gilzean is closer than he thought, the Scot latching on to the ball and hurdling one outstretched Brazilian boot, then another, before sidestepping the outrushing Felix, stumbling as he does so but swiftly righting himself and turning through 180 degrees to poke a low, twenty-yard shot into the temporarily unguarded goal.

'Do you like gold, boys?' Stein says at half-time as the players look to him. Then Shankly takes over. 'Well,' he says, 'the ball's a lump of gold for the next forty-five minutes.' Busby removes his pipe from mouth to conclude, 'So don't give it away.'

It is a delicious, warm feeling for the Scots to be ahead for a second time in a final with Brazil and with the game progressing like a chess match between two grandmasters – conducted sportingly but with a nerve-tingling desire for victory underpinning every move – the Scots appear to have the measure of the South Americans. Then Moncur challenges

Clodoaldo outside the Scottish penalty area and Rudi Glöckner, the East German referee, rather severely awards a free-kick. Rivellino prepares to take it from directly in front of goal but Clark, behind a six-man defensive wall, appears to have both sides of the goal covered – and he does – but Rivellino's turbo-charged, right-footed strike whistles through the wall and under Clark's crossbar before the goalkeeper can even think about considering how to go about reacting. Five minutes on, Gérson dances diagonally through the midfield, ball at his feet, then turns with a deft, ballroom grace that contrasts with his subsequent, explosive left-footed shot, one that swirls through half a dozen players from both sides to its destination three inches inside the foot of Clark's left-hand post.

There are four minutes remaining and the Brazilians now pack their defence solidly. There is no way through for the holders and as the seconds tick away the touchline becomes thronged with more and more spectators, ready to rush on to the field and acclaim the Brazilians on the bright Azteca field, with the Scots already consigned to the shadows.

'Luck was following us,' Carlos Alberto, the Brazil captain, says forty-five minutes after the final whistle, when he is finally freed of the all-engulfing crowd. 'Scotland could just as easily have won this game. Our friends matched us for conviction and skill and good fortune was on our side.'

Shankly is unequivocal in his verdict. 'I am bitterly disappointed because I know the players we have with us now are good enough to have won the championship.' Stein adds, 'They are still the champions in my eyes.' Busby shakes his head, 'I feel that we haven't been overthrown. We've abdicated.'

Acclaim pours down on the Brazilians like liquid gold as the Scottish players, drained by defeat, finally feel the effects of the sun and the weeks and weeks of preparation and playing in heat. Their games in Mexico have been colourful and their football has danced. Even in a tournament overheated in every way, the Scots' presence has given this World Cup an extra degree of warmth.

CULTURED FOOTBALL

The Taunus Mountains provide an appropriate backdrop as Billy Bremner, the Scotland captain, holds court at the team's hotel the morning after the 1–1 draw with Yugoslavia. Peaking at the right time, Bremner stresses, is the key to winning World Cups, which is why, he says, the team's rather flat performance against the eastern European side, midway through the tournament, has left neither him nor Willie Ormond, the manager, overly concerned.

There is an unlikely maturity about this young Scotland team, evinced by Bremner's unforced declaration that he, Denis Law and Jimmy Johnstone, as the senior players in the squad, are behind the idea for team officials to request that their new team hotel remove all stocks of alcohol from within its premises. Peter Reckit, the Scots' team psychologist, had advised strongly that the Scotland squad should switch hotels after their three matches in the opening group stage so they are now resident at the Erbismuhle Hotel in Rus an der Weil, close to Frankfurt. The squad's previous residence was just as well situated for their next fixtures, all in northern West Germany but, 'You have no idea what a difference to morale this makes,' Reckit says. 'Players can get bored if they stay too long in the same place. They like change. Remaining within the rather limited confines of one hotel, any hotel, can transform even the most elegant surroundings into the equivalent of a dull, grey prison. It can be like entrapment within a Cubist painting – the same shapes and structures that were once so welcoming and interesting now seeming like barriers. I could go on . . . Shall I?'

The request from Scotland officials, soon after their arrival, to remove all alcohol from the hotel has wrong-footed Manfred Schwartz, the hotel manager, a rotund Bavarian, who openly admits that he had ordered in extra stocks of drink to cater for his distinguished guests on the basis of the reputation of Scottish footballers enjoying a drink or twenty post-match and, sometimes, pre-match. Even as Bremner speaks, a lorry is drawing up in the hotel court-yard and a couple of draymen are working assiduously, in best Germanic fashion, to load multiple crates of beer, four dozen cases of champagne and even more of whisky into the vehicle. They can be seen clearly from the courtyard off to the side of the hotel where Bremner, on this steamy summer's day, is deep in discussion with the press. A wistful expression at the sight of the alcohol being removed flits across his features as, involuntarily, he licks his lips slowly in a moment of reverie, but he is soon back on the topic of how nothing is going to distract him and his squad-mates from their ultimate goal.

'No, there is no question of boredom setting in,' Bremner says in relation to a reporter's question on the effect of deciding to water down the strength of the post-match refreshments. 'We are professionals. Why would we get upset about having a few quiet nights in and around the hotel when there is the chance of making progress in the World Cup? I just don't see it as any sort of dilemma and I wouldn't understand the player who was prepared to gamble his fitness and preparation just for the sake of a few drinks. You can drink all you want after the World Cup but, honestly, the boys aren't really thinking about missing out on having a few drinks anyway. Their focus is frightening at times and they are determined to make the most of this chance. They have got the whole thing entirely in perspective.'

The now departing lorry, weighed down by its unwanted cargo, is one manifestation of the players' serious intent.

Meanwhile, to the rear of the hotel, several Scottish players are gathered interestedly around an outsize chessboard with pieces several feet in height, as Jim Holton, the gargantuan centre-half, and Eric Schaedler, the full-back, ponder their next moves. Willie Ormond moves easily among his men, taking time to draw players aside for individual chats. 'He's great, the manager,' Bremner says. 'He just helps you get your head right.' It seems almost ludicrously inappropriate, now, to quiz the captain on the rumours that had abounded after the Scots' modest opening performance against Zaire in relation to the players allegedly having nicknamed their manager Donny Osmond, after the sickly sweet, fresh-faced, teenage singing star who has been cloyingly clogging up the airwaves for the past year or two. It seems equally inappropriate to ask

Bremner to confirm that he and others had actively and furtively sought tactical advice from Jock Stein – in West Germany working as a television pundit – and that Bremner himself is as involved in making the key decisions as his manager. Watching Ormond move authoritatively around the grounds of the team hotel is almost enough to dispel such rumours.

If the manager's reputation has grown apace during this tournament, then so too has that of Bremner. 'Bremner may turn out to be the best player in this World Cup,' Pelé has said after the Scots' victory over Brazil in their second group game. 'He is an inspiration to his side, a free organizer and the outstanding improviser and leader of men of all the countries.' High praise indeed, given that Johan Cruyff, the outstanding Dutch forward, and West Germany's libero, Franz Beckenbauer, would seem the Stirling man's natural rivals for such an accolade.

'That was very kind of Pelé,' Bremner states calmly and in statesmanlike fashion, enviously eyeing the chess game to which he would clearly prefer to be giving his attention rather than dealing with a collection of quote-hungry reporters. 'But, and I do mean this, we have to ignore individual praise and I would say that to any of the players here. The day we start attaching too much importance to how we are regarded as individuals is the day we will cease to be a force at World Cups. Without each other we are nothing. Every man in this squad has his role to play. I'll also need to dig Pelé up about that next time I see him.'

With Poland, Sweden and West Germany on the horizon, in the new format of a second group stage following the first one, Bremner is clearly charged by the challenge. 'Zaire were better than people think,' Bremner says of the African side that provided the opposition in the Scots' first group game, 'and the Brazilians and the Yugoslavs gave us a stiff test. But we have always found that once you qualify from your initial group in a World Cup, that is when the action really starts. It's also important to remember that this is a very young squad. Only myself, Denis Law, Jimmy Johnstone and David Hay were involved in the last World Cup and maybe that's why there wasn't a lot expected of this year's team – but we might still surprise a few people.'

An attractive, blonde, serving girl, trussed up in traditional costume, shimmies over to Bremner's table to serve him with a drink, attracting the attention, as one, of the all-male Scottish press pack, but Bremner, so deeply involved in reflecting upon the World Cup, doesn't even notice her. 'We are going to win this competition or I will want to know the reason why not,' he goes on, drawing back the attention of the hacks through the forcefulness and resolve with which he enunciates his words. 'We are afraid of no one.' Time to enjoy his fresh drink, a sparkling glass of amber liquid. 'Apple juice,' Bremner says with a laugh, 'and that's as strong a drink as I'll take before we get to Munich and the final.'

· 1974 · 1974 · 1974 · 1974 · 1974 · 1974 · 1974 · 1974 · 1974 · 1974 ·

Gusts of booing sweep across the stands and terraces inside the Rheinstadion as Bremner and his team-mates get down to work in Düsseldorf during the first of the three matches in their all-European, second-stage group. The 67,000 West Germans present, who have spent hours queuing to buy tickets for this match in anticipation of watching their team roll on toward the final, do not like what they are seeing as Scotland determinedly hold the hosts at bay. Beckenbauer, the West German captain, had gesticulated at his own fans earlier in the tournament when they grew restless during West Germany's dull display against Australia and here, again, the 'Kaiser' looks less than imperious as he is hustled out of his usual, steady stride by the bustling Bremner and the harrying Hay in the Scotland midfield. Shortly before half-time Paul Breitner, the West German full-back, escapes the attentions of the Scots and eases forward for a long-range shot that has David Harvey, the Scotland goalkeeper, scurrying across goal to palm the ball around the post but it is a rare sight of goal for the team representing the host nation.

As the West Germans troop off at half-time, those among their fans who are situated close to the mouth of the players' tunnel rub fingers and thumbs together, a reference to the much-publicized dispute over bonuses that has soured the players' relations with their public since the beginning of the tournament and that bitterness will not go away until the Germans fully prove their worth on the pitch, rather than at the negotiating table: team members had threatened not to play at all unless their prospective bonus payments were increased. 'Are you still on strike?' one angry, middle-aged fan yells at his team; doing so, bizarrely, in English, for the benefit of the Scots.

It is all very pleasing for Ormond's team, who were not only containing the Germans in that first half but also proving a constant threat to them. The manager's decision to replace Kenny Dalglish – one of the few disappointments during the first group stage – with Tommy Hutchison has taken the Germans by surprise and they are struggling to cope with the dual threat of Hutchison and Willie Morgan, on the left and right wings respectively, firing in crosses for Joe Jordan, the tall and rumbustious striker, who has Peter Lorimer operating alongside him. Breitner and Berti Vogts have rarely done so much scurrying around after opponents and Katsche Schwarzenbeck, the German centre-half, once described as 'half human, half bull', has met his attacking equivalent in the shape of the fearless, front-toothless Jordan. The Kaiser, meanwhile, has looked increasingly like a bedraggled aristocrat roused from his bed in the middle of the night to watch his country pile going up in flames.

Scotland's own bonus dispute is now long behind them; rumours that the players had used knives from the breakfast table at their hotel to scrape off the trademark white stripes of a well-known boot manufacturer after failing to reach agreement over payments were proven correct when the players took to the field for their initial matches. Rather than this being an indicator of discord and dissatisfaction inside the squad, their blacked-out boots are talismanic of solidarity among a set of players willing to back each other up in all circumstances, on and off the field.

'If patriotism is silly,' Hay has said before the game with West Germany, 'then, yes, we're silly. When we go on to the field for Scotland, we're ready to give blood. Of course we'd like a lot of money but even without it we'll play until we drop.' That sums up the spirit in this Scottish side and when that passion is soldered on to the traditional ball-playing skills of the Scottish footballer it is a fearsome combination. Bremner – memorably described by Mulamba Ndaye, the Zaire player, as a 'wild animal' and punched in the face by an unnerved Roberto Rivellino after the Brazilian had tired of the Scotland midfield player's almost actionable harassment of him – is again epitomizing the ideal, chivvying and chasing the elegant

German ball-players Rainer Bonhof and Bernd Hölzenbein so assiduously that they resemble a couple of postmen fending off the attentions of an angry dog.

The second half continues in the same vein as the first, the home crowd becoming ever more restless in fear of a second, possibly crippling, debilitating defeat, to go with the shock setback their team suffered against East Germany last week. Tension grips the crowd as Scotland go close to scoring when a header from Jordan, connecting with a Hutchison cross, scrapes the outside of Sepp Maier's left-hand post after sixty-one minutes. Eight minutes from time, the Germans, now being willed on by a desperate crowd, almost nick it when Gerd Müller slides into the six-yard box and prods the ball goal-ward but Harvey is equal to his efforts with a fine reflex save to deflect the ball around the post. A tight, stuffy match concludes 0–0.

'Scotland really are among the favourites for this tournament,' Helmut Schoen, the West Germany manager, says after the match. 'We have known that for some time and the events today only confirmed our suspicions. It puzzled me before the World Cup that the Scots had not seen themselves in the way that the rest of the world sees them but maybe after today they will. Yes, they are a young team without many of the famous names from the past but they are excellent players. Maybe you Scots have had so much success in the past that you are still intoxicated by it and cannot focus on this new Scotland team but I must tell you that they are very good indeed.'

Ormond, delighted with a performance that provides Scotland with a springboard to the final, is also keen to extol his players' qualities. 'Every time you ask this team to get their teeth into something, they just bite and bite,' he says. 'I will be asking them to show their teeth for me again in our next two games and I know that they will do it for me.'

Those forthcoming matches, against Poland and Sweden, now look exceedingly inviting for Bremner and his sober, sensible team-mates, who showed that some of the lessons learned from the chessboard at the team hotel could be applied equally well on the football field.

· 1974 · 1974 · 1974 · 1974 · 1974 · 1974 · 1974 · 1974 · 1974 · 1974 ·

The Germans like to do things on a large scale; they always have done. As the Scots, a dozen hours after facing the competition's hosts, take a relaxed Thursday-morning trip into Frankfurt, huge cut-out images of the West Germany players are to be seen everywhere; suspended from every available spur that juts from the city's shiny, spanking-new buildings. The West German postwar 'economic miracle' has seen Frankfurt, the country's financial hub, enjoy even greater prosperity than most other parts of the nation and the Germans' commercial acumen has made this the first World Cup to have brought money and sponsorship to the fore. The outsize images of the players that overhang the streets below are for the dual purposes of advertising and for the propaganda of presenting the German players as the giants of this tournament; its dominant force and its winners in waiting.

The Scottish squad's efforts to embrace commercialism have proved a good deal less slick. The players, keen to take advantage of opportunities to make money, appointed an agent to try to maximize their earning potential – though it was at that point that they began to tread a path that diverged from the one Franz Beckenbauer and his squad-mates have taken. The Scots' agent is one Bob Bain, a stage comedian, a former compere for The Beatles, among other acts, and who, in the weeks prior to the squad's departure for West Germany, is nicknamed by them the 'Tartan Pimpernel' for his elusiveness, both in a physical sense and, once cornered, for his vagueness on the subject of the players' expected earnings. Telephone discussions between Bremner and Bain have been strained, to say the least, with the Scotland captain, while deep in discussion, seizing hold of the telephone wire in a way that looked less than promising for Bain's physical well-being. When the agent finally does turn up for a meeting, he and Bremner disagree pointedly in front of the press and Bain, a rotund, cigar-chomping individual, appears lucky that there are too many witnesses present for the discussions not to edge into a confrontation that might have been damaging to his health.

It is soon apparent to the Scottish players that they will not be building up a mountain of cash through their participation in this World Cup. The players have even refused to wear their Roary Super Scot watches – each emblazoned with the SFA team mascot: a cartoon lion wearing a Scotland strip, an open, smiling facial expression and a shaggy mane – not on the grounds of taste but in protest at their lack of earnings from tournament spin-offs. The new maturity that is guiding this squad has, though, seen even that difficult aspect of their tilt at this World Cup being transformed into something to their benefit.

'After all the hassles involved with trying to get some extra money together for the boys,' Jim Holton, the centre-back, explains, 'we decided on a different approach. Thanks to our discussions with the Tartan Pimpernel having been made so public, and with the punters getting restless because the press were saying we were money-grabbers, we just decided to turn our backs on it all and concentrate on the football. Other than a hundred-pound voucher from House of Fraser and a new set of clothes from Man at C&A, we've not made anything out of this tournament but money isn't everything, is it?

'We have to accept that we are a small nation compared to West Germany and that we could never earn as much as their players. They say that the Germans will earn a bonus of £25,000 a head if they win the World Cup . . .' Holton's voice trails off and a faraway look enters his eyes but he quickly rights himself, '. . . but, eh, we've decided were not interested in money, that it's not worth the hassle and it's too big a distraction from playing the game. Besides, we're quite happy for the SFA to keep any money they make from the tourney and they'll know what's best to do with it, whether that's ploughing it into youth football, or refereeing or whatever. We know that if it's with the SFA it's in good hands.'

With the tawdry issue of monetary reward put behind them, the Scots have made a conscious effort to concentrate on more elevated matters to help bind together the squad. Their journey into Frankfurt this late morning is not, as might be expected of football players, to enable them to carry out some fun souvenir shopping. Instead, they are making their way to the Frankfurt Festhalle for a special lunchtime concert; their attendance there being at the behest of Bremner, who, as their captain, has insisted that even the most reluctant attendees come along rather than lounge around the hotel pool. The concert in question is a performance of Beethoven's Ninth Symphony by the Vienna Philharmonic Orchestra, conducted by Leonard Bernstein. 'Trust me,' Bremner tells the squad, 'when these guys are in town for something like this, you cannot afford to miss it.'

Arriving early, the players mill around in the foyer, barely recognized by their fellow concert-goers, who are, in the main, well-heeled and late-middle-aged representatives of the upper echelons of Frankfurt society. One or two of the squad note, disinterestedly, that a bar is already open, even pre-noon, to serve refreshments to particularly thirsty seekers after culture but the players' attention is soon held by an exhibition of artefacts related to Beethoven.

One sketch of the maestro shows him as a stocky, squat figure in top hat and long coat, wearing a determined expression, jaw jutting out, as he strolls the streets of Vienna. 'Hey, skipper,' yells Jimmy Johnstone, 'he looks a bit like yourself.' Guffaws of laughter greet this observation and Bremner, always happy to join in with jollity, especially when someone is having a joke at his expense, keenly smiles at Johnstone's remark. Another exhibit is of the original bill, in German, announcing the first performance of the Ninth Symphony in May 1824. 'That looks a bit like our contract with the Tartan Pimpernel,' joshes Erich Schaedler and again the company enjoy much laughter. A painting of Friedrich Wilhelm III, the Prussian king to whom Beethoven dedicated the symphony, wearing a stern, wry expression, draws the remark from Holton, 'Hey, Billy, he looks a bit like Beckenbauer after you'd finished with him last night!' More laughter and Willie Morgan adds, 'Like the gear, though. He looks like a right raver. Get it on, Wilhelm.'

The king, who does indeed bear a resemblance to Beckenbauer and with whom the German player shares his habitually haughty, confident expression, is showing off a magnificent pair of gold epaulettes on a buttoned-up, scarlet tunic, with a high neckband, plus various items of military insignia, including an Iron Cross, no less. It's not that far removed from the best of mid-seventies youth clobber, as

Morgan, chief wearer of the latest gear among the squad, has perceptively pointed out.

The sound of an electronic bell rents the air, followed by several crisp words in German and, as concert-goers set down empty glasses and coffee cups, it is clear the management wish people to take their seats. There are twenty minutes remaining before the noon performance but Bremner, anxious not to create a bad impression on the part of the Scotland squad, says, 'When in Rome –' and leads the players into the auditorium. An hour and a half later, the Scots emerge, blinking, into the early afternoon.

'The world looks entirely different after witnessing and hearing something like that,' Bremner says. Peter Lorimer adds, 'That was stupendous.' David Harvey concurs, 'Absolutely life-changing.' Jimmy Johnstone, in raptures, comments, 'Pure brilliant. Where do I get his LPs?' The uplifting effects of being present at this performance, this nourishing dose of culture, is another welcome boost to the players in getting through the remainder of the tournament.

· 1974 · 1974 · 1974 · 1974 · 1974 · 1974 · 1974 · 1974 · 1974 · 1974 ·

Later this Thursday evening, having returned from the concert, Johnstone and Bremner are sharing the hotel's hi-fi, each with his own set of headphones like huge, black ear muffs, listening intently to a Mozart piano concerto, while around them their team-mates quietly play, variously, backgammon, chess, draughts and battleships. Martin Buchan is with the hotel's resident band, joining them on guitar; classical Spanish is his speciality but he can turn his hand to more popular numbers.

'If we keep our minds sharp when we are off the field,' Peter Lorimer says, 'it should help us to be even more alert when we are playing football.'

It is into this oasis of calm that Willie Ormond hurries to tap Bremner on the shoulder and usher him away into a side room. 'There's a problem,' a visibly flustered Ormond says. 'German television has put out a programme this evening portraying us as a bunch of drunks who can't keep our hands off the booze. They are saying that wee Jimmy was found in the gutter paralytic last night and that he is about to be sent home and that the boys are caning the booze at the hotel every night.' Bremner thinks hard. 'Have you seen this programme?' Ormond replies in the negative. 'I just heard about it from a pressman, who phoned through. Apparently they are going to repeat it at ten o'clock tonight.'

At that hour, one at which the Scotland squad are normally tucked up in bed in preparation for the next day's training, a private room at the Erbismuhle Hotel is reserved for the Scottish party to watch the half-hour sports broadcast, which leads, as promised, with a story about the Scots' alleged drunkenness. The film begins with the camera focusing on a table laden with bottles of champagne, beer and schnapps and then pans out to the entire Scotland squad gathered around it.

'That's here at the hotel,' Ormond says, 'That's the stuff they put on for us when they gave us our welcoming reception, remember? The thing they're not showing is that hardly anybody bothered with it and that most of the boys settled for a coffee or a Coke, or a cup of tea.'

The film, with a sober German voiceover, cuts to shots of Scottish fans guzzling bottles of beer in central Frankfurt and of locals hurrying by on the other side of the street, trying to avoid them. The footage switches to Jimmy Johnstone going from hotel to team bus, tie askew, chortling away giddily and holding on to a team-mate's shoulder. 'That's just me having a laugh,' Johnstone says.

The film concludes and the programme switches to a discussion in the studio between the presenter and two German journalists. 'What are they saying?' Ormond says, turning to Bernhard Klodt, the translator attached to the team. 'Well, they are saying that nobody should be surprised about this, that it is traditional for the Scots to train on an alcoholic diet and that it's nothing new. "What is a Scotsman without a drink?", one of these fellows here is saying. They are saying, also, that the Scottish team is a good one, very accomplished . . . at drinking.' The panel in the TV studio are seen laughing heartily at this little joke. 'They are saying that Jimmy will be very happy that he is being sent home because, like most Scottish players, he likes to spend his summers in an English pub – that's how they put it – rather than playing football.'

The discussion draws to an end and is to be followed by a succession of images of West German goals being banged in during the tournament. 'Switch it off,' Ormond orders. 'Right boys, get to your beds and we'll talk about this in the morning.'

· 1974 · 1974 · 1974 · 1974 · 1974 · 1974 · 1974 · 1974 · 1974 · 1974 ·

A crowd of around 8,000 assembles the following morning for the Scots' scheduled open-doors friendly match at Neu Isenburg, near Frankfurt, against a local amateur select. Originally planned as a combination of a training match and a PR exercise to maintain good relations with the Scots' hosts in this part of West Germany, it now – in the wake of the previous evening's television report – comes under the scrutiny of the world's football press with journalists and a phalanx of photographers following every move made by the Scots. 'If they want a story,' Ormond says under his breath, 'they will get a story.'

As the players take the field for their warm-up, Johnstone sways, balances on one leg and appears about to topple over before being caught by two team-mates, who transport him on to the pitch and deposit him on the wing, where he stands, motionless, eyes closed, head pointed to the ground. An audible, collective gasp goes around the crowd. The photographers scurry to the touchline closest to the winger and snap away at him. Then come the two Scottish trainers, each laden down by two crates of brown beer bottles. Johnstone suddenly perks up at the sound of the clinking crates and as the trainers enter the field, he is the first to get to them and hauls out two bottles, tipping them, one after the other, bottoms up, into his mouth, before tossing them away and suddenly jolting into life, looking for the ball as he sprints away. His team-mates follow suit, suddenly lively after their visit to the trainers' supplies. An 11–2 victory over the local side follows, with no quarter asked or given.

Collared by the press afterward, Ormond is asked about his reaction to the documentary and about when Johnstone is to be sent home. 'Does Johnstone look like a man about to be sent home?' he says. 'Would he be playing in this game and scoring two goals if he was about to be sent home? As for the programme you mention, the German television doesn't make any sense to us.' Asked why he allowed his players to drink beer before playing football, Ormond tells the querulous reporters that the team are allowed a good drink before every training session. He doesn't mention that the brown beer bottles had been filled with water.

'We're looking forward to a rare old night out tonight,' Bremner tells the set of scribblers who gather around him as he stands on the edge of the pitch, beads of sweat trickling down his forehead. His words make them crowd in closer, anxious not to miss any details of the Scots' forthcoming nocturnal excursion. 'That was a good workout and we thank the players and officials of Neu Isenburg for their help in arranging this fixture and being such worthy opponents. So that's us done our preparation for the day and we'll now go back to the hotel and relax before hitting the town.'

The press men write down furiously every word in their notebooks. 'Where will you be going tonight?' one of them boldly asks Bremner. 'Well,' he replies, 'we haven't quite decided yet. We'll be going into Frankfurt and there is such a variety of venues there but we've narrowed it down a bit. It'll either be *The Way We Were*, which seems a bit soppy but has got a bit of baseball in it; or *Thunderbolt and Lightfoot* or *The Great Gatsby*, Robert Redford again. I would have to ask you, quite seriously, has there ever been a greater decade for cinema than this one, the seventies, even though we're barely halfway through it? All of these, I've heard, are terrific films and we'll make sure we catch one of them tonight or, if we get out early evening, we might really over-indulge and watch two of them. Okay, lads, thanks very much.' He turns and heads happily for the rural ground's poky little dressing room, leaving the attendant representatives of the world's media thoroughly perplexed.

On the coach back to their neat hotel in its woodland surrounds, the Scots see a giant poster at the side of the autobahn featuring two cartoon football teams, one in white shirts with black shorts, clearly representing West Germany, the other in navy blue shirts and white shorts. A player in blue has the ball on his toes in front of goal but is clearly being distracted by one of his white-shirted opponents, who is proffering an outsize bottle of whisky. One of the white-shirted defenders is about to take advantage by whisking the ball away. 'Scotch whisky,' the poster reads in English, 'best in the world. Irresistible – just ask the Scots themselves.' Bremner, in the front seat of the coach, sighs resignedly. 'What can you do?' he says. Half a mile down this near-featureless stretch of auto-bahn, the poster again looms large, and again a little bit farther on, then a fourth time before the coach turns off the motorway.

'You know,' Ormond says, 'that is supposed to be an adver-tisement for whisky but they're not actually mentioning any brand. I wonder who has put those up? I think it's the Germans themselves; in fact, I'm convinced of it. They've been rattled and they think we can get to the final at their expense so that advertisement and the television show are their ways of putting out some propaganda against us. I'm sure of it.'

· 1974 · 1974 · 1974 · 1974 · 1974 · 1974 · 1974 · 1974 · 1974 · 1974 ·

Poland are the Scots' next opponents. 'We Scottish players talk too much,' Bremner tells the press before the game at the Waldstadion, Frankfurt on an uncomfortably hot day. 'I have told the lads not to snipe at referees and to bow and scrape after a foul, even though it may be out of the Scottish char-acter. I am the worst culprit. We have to change our ways and we must not show the studs or be too rash in the tackle or we will be in trouble.'

His pre-match talk looks to have worked when Andrzej Szarmach, the Poland forward, looks for Lorimer to foul him in the penalty area but Lorimer makes a point of withdrawing from the tackle, holding back and throwing his arms in the air to signify his determination to stand back and not make any contact. It matters little to Rudi Glöckner, the East German referee, who, with the whistle pursed between his lips, sprints for the penalty spot, then turns through 180 degrees and jogs backward to the goal-line, arm still outstretched toward the penalty spot. Scotland players confront him but are hauled quickly away by Bremner. Lorimer has been the most vociferous among the protesters and is called back by the referee. 'Apologize, Peter,' Bremner, says through gritted teeth, 'Apologize!'

Lorimer, one of the more relaxed and placid members of the squad, does so as he reaches Glöckner. 'Sorry, ref,' he says, 'don't know what came over me.'

Glöckner, a grim, grey-faced, hawk-like man, with a brilliantine short-back-and-sides, glares at the Scot. 'Sorry, sorry, sorry,' he barks in crisp, curt English, 'you think that enough is? You hearing me, these comradely Polish players here will get no bonus money at all – even if the competition they win. They amateur, you know. Financial reward out of question! It is same for the wonderful footballers from mein own DDR. Yet all I hear about from you capitalists is disputes on money. I am surprised people do not spit on you in the street! And you – you dispute my decision? You are spoilt, spoilt. You hear? So take this.' He brandishes a yellow card at a now thoroughly bamboozled Lorimer. Kazimierz Deyna scores with the penalty kick.

Two minutes from half-time, Lorimer eases on to a pass from Hay, glides past Jerzy Gorgon, the medieval-looking

Poland centre-back, dummies Jan Tomaszewski, the goalkeeper, and fires a shot high into the net. Glöckner rushes up and signals for offside even though Lorimer has run from in front of the defence and Glöckner's linesman has made no signal to suggest anything wrong with the goal.

Early in the second half, the Poles score again when Robert Gadocha's corner is headed into the net by Grzegorz Lato. 'Fine players, these Poles, no?' Glöckner suggests to Holton as he glides backward toward the centre circle, as if on a unicycle. 'Discipline, dedication and lack of decadent distraction make them good team.' With six minutes remaining, the Scots' fate is sealed when Glöckner awards another soft penalty after Holton collides with Henryk Kasperczak inside the penalty area. 'That was never a penalty, ref!' Holton yells. 'Conditions determine consciousness,' Glöckner retorts. 'A warm man, like you in the West, cannot understand a cold man.' Again he quells further protest by flashing a yellow card in Holton's direction. Deyna, again, is unerringly accurate from the penalty spot.

This is what the World Cup is like. You think things are going swimmingly and that you are about to surface with a smile, only to discover that you are being pulled down by currents beyond your control.

'There were a few tears in the dressing room,' Bremner admits after a defeat that ushers the Scots out of the tournament and renders their final fixture, with Sweden, the next best thing to a friendly. 'Let's face it, we're an emotional race. Willie Ormond more or less told us it had been a privilege for those teams we've played to have been on the same pitch as us and I think everyone has seen that there are forces at work in these modern World Cups that have nothing to do with the game of football itself.'

It is not much good to the players of 1974 but the lessons learned from this tournament ensure that Scotland are now much less likely to fall victim to dirty tricks from a host nation – whenever that may happen again in a World Cup finals.

TURNING THE WORLD UPSIDE DOWN

There has always been a degree of doubt as to whether or not Ally MacLeod has ever said the golden words of promise that are attributed to him. The Scottish nation has become euphoric in anticipation of the team bringing home the World Cup from the finals in Argentina and MacLeod has been instrumental in creating this febrile state of excitement, doing nothing to dampen the atmosphere or to quash the general belief in the country that little more is demanded of Scotland than to turn up in Argentina for the trophy to be theirs. Yet though the general belief that Scotland will bring back the World Cup, few fans can point to a specific statement from MacLeod or to a moment when MacLeod has declared himself pleased to go on the record and confirm that this is his belief. It all seems to have come about more as a general feeling, kept glowingly warm by the bellows of the media, than from a specific declaration from MacLeod himself.

MacLeod has certainly said, vaguely, before the tournament, 'We will win a medal.' That, though, suggests that the manager is confident his team can come at least third and is hugely different from expecting to become world champions, given that the World Cup's third/fourth-place play-off is viewed, inside and outside the game, as the next best thing to a dead rubber. Finishing third in the World Cup is a long way short of first, or even second.

The cloud of doubt over this issue is why, with Scotland having qualified for the second round of the 1978 World Cup, Ally MacLeod is leading around 200 newspaper journalists, drawn from around the globe, plus two Scottish television crews, toward the foothills of the Andes this early, mid-June, Tuesday morning. Four donkeys and their handlers, some Argentinian government minders and Francisco Vaira, a tour guide assigned to the Scottish national football squad for the '78 World Cup, complete the party. Strapped across the back of one donkey is an outsize loudhailer; the next beast has the burden of a large, white, cloth banner and the rear two are held in tandem by the ladder that is stretched across their backs.

A gauzy fog is lifting when the party reaches the part of the mountain range closest to the city of Mendoza, where Scotland have been based in recent days. Vaira leads his charges a farther quarter of a mile until they reach a path that runs for 400 yards up the mountainside to a natural shelf that has been created where the rock has been worn smooth. 'Over many years,' Vaira says to the assembled throng, once everyone has managed to find a space for themselves on the platform, 'people have come here to enjoy the view, to drink deep of the fresher air when the heat of summer gets too much and to take away with them the good luck that, our folk wisdom says, comes to those whose feet follow in the steps of those of our ancestors who stood in this place before us. We are with them and they are with us. It is a beautiful link between the past and the present and it is said to augur well for future fortunes. Now, without further ado, I will place you in the capable hands of the man you have come to hear, Señor Ally MacLeod.'

Vaira steps back and, with the assistance of the donkey-handlers, unloads the loudhailer, the banner and the ladder. 'Escocia – Campeónes' is written in blue letters on the banner's white cloth and, in case anyone is unsure, an immediate translation is written underneath: 'Scotland – Champions'. After a bit of a struggle it is taped to the rock-face and cameras whirr as MacLeod ascends the ladder, takes the loudhailer from Vaira and, resplendent in a Scotland top and tracksuit trousers, stands elevated above those who are waiting for his words.

'Friends,' he begins, 'thank you all for coming and let me say how happy I am to welcome you to my official press conference ahead of our vital second-group-phase match with Austria tomorrow. Some of you may think I am lucky to be here. You saw us lose to Peru and draw with Iran and you immediately consigned me to what someone once called the dustbin of history. Well, I have to say that you were half-right but really you were quite wrong; not even half-wrong.'

At this, the pressmen stop scribbling notes and, instead, look up from their notebooks to exchange quizzical glances; especially puzzled are those unused to MacLeod's sometimes idiosyncratic way with words. With a nose that he compares often to Concorde, the sharp-beaked, supersonic airliner, a mane of floppy, unkempt golden hair and a light, sing-song voice, MacLeod is unlike the other managers at the tournament, who glower and snap back at journalists and who talk only of tactics, fitness tests and their players' mental preparation for each game. The Scot has, throughout his managerial career, been an unpredictable firework of a manager, willing to expound on any subject that is thrown at him, and though his relations with the press had turned icy prior to Sunday's 3–0 victory over Holland – a near-miraculous result that ushered the Scots into the World Cup's second phase by the skin of their teeth – MacLeod's natural ebullience is returning, slowly, on the back of that unexpected success.

'You see behind me a banner that reveals nothing but the truth, the whole truth, the, eh, the absolute truth and all that,' he continues. 'People have been asking, "Did Ally really say that Scotland would win the World Cup?" Well, there you have it, look.' He stretches out his right hand and half-turns toward the banner, temporarily losing his balance on the ladder's narrow metal platform and, for one nasty moment, the Scotland manager appears in danger of tumbling down the Andean cliff-face before he can do anything else in this World Cup, but he rights himself and adds, 'That's it, there it is: Scotland to be world champions.' He sweeps back some stray locks that have fallen across his forehead as a result of his little slip. 'That's what I'm saying. I want to prove I am the best manager in the world and to do that I have to win the World Cup. It's really quite simple if you think about it. I think you would also all agree that if we play the way we played against Holland we can easily go on and win the thing.

'Now a lot of criticism came our way when we stuttered a wee bit through our first two games but these were really just warm-ups for us. We lulled the Dutch into a false sense of security by looking not so good against Peru and Iran and by the time they woke up to us it was too late. Did you see Alan Rough, our goalkeeper, during the second half against Holland? He was sitting on the ground watching the game because it was being played in their half of the field. It was as if he was down the park for a casual kick-about on a hot summer's Sunday afternoon. By the way, I thought Argentina was supposed to be a hot country. My goodness but it doesn't half get cold at night here, doesn't it?

'Anyway, that's by the by. Now where was I? Yes, that's right, we are going to win the World Cup. Now I want all you snappers to get a good photo of that banner and get it sent around the world with the news. Let there be no doubt – we mean business.'

With this, MacLeod lifts the loudhailer waist-high and asks Vaira, 'Which direction is Buenos Aires?' Then, pointing the loudhailer toward the horizon, and raising it to his lips, MacLeod begins, 'Hear this, Argentina! Scotland *are* going to win the World Cup! Do you hear? Scotland *are* going to be world champions. Get ready for the twenty-fifth of June. We will be in Buenos Aires for the final and whether it is Argentina, Brazil, Peru or Poland we face, we are going to win. In fact you could put out on to the field a team that day combined from the best players that all four of those countries can offer and we will still win. It is not so much a question of "Will Scotland win the World Cup?" It is more, "Who can stop us? And how?" I think I have made myself clear.'

With that, MacLeod dismounts from the ladder and hands the loudhailer to Vaira. The journalists swarm around him, jabbing questions in his direction, but MacLeod answers only to say, 'You've got your story now. You could hardly get a better story than that, could you? If you want to know how it is going to happen, then the best thing you can do is to watch our matches. It's that simple.'

· 1978 · 1978 · 1978 · 1978 · 1978 · 1978 · 1978 · 1978 · 1978 · 1978 ·

The Scotland manager is no less voluble in the team dressing room prior to the match with Austria. 'I've just received the Austrian line-up,' he says to his players, shortly before kick-off in the Chateau Carreras Stadium, Córdoba, on the day after his trip to the Andes. MacLeod has a rectangular piece of paper in his hand with the team lines for this afternoon's match typed upon it. His players raise their heads to hear what he has to say, in particular if he has any last-minute tips to give them about an Austrian team of which they know only a little.

'Well,' MacLeod says,' looking at the list of names in front of him, 'the goalkeeper is top class, a terrific shot-stopper; the two full-backs are exceptionally pacy, so they can attack and defend up and down the flanks all day; the central defenders are rock solid. Then there is so much cleverness in the four midfield players they should open their own university and the front two have got everything you need for putting the ball in the pokey hat; one of them wins everything in the air for the other guy, who is the best goal-scorer in Europe.

'That's the Scottish team. Now, as for the Austrians . . .' and so saying he scrolls down the left-hand side of the team sheet with his index finger, 'I've never heard of their goal-keeper, don't know any of their defenders. I do know a couple of their midfield players but they are useless. Up front they've got this wee guy, Hans Krankl, who should be selling pretzels under the Prater's Ferris wheel: he's a bit fly, a bit streetwise, but he's got nothing about him that Martin and Tam can't handle.' With this, MacLeod tears the team sheet in two and rips the half containing the Austrian names into tiny pieces before throwing it into the bin. 'Lads,' he says, 'you're playing nobody; nothing. There's only one team on this park today, only one team that can win, only one team that will win.' With that, as if on cue, the referee's bell rings and the players rise to make their way out on to the field of play.

Five minutes have passed when Bruce Rioch uses the outside of his right boot to send a free-kick from the right into the Austrian penalty area. The ball whirrs over the heads of half a dozen players before Tom Forsyth, unmarked at the back post, plants a header past Fritz Koncilia in the Austrian goal. 'Easy this game, isn't it?' MacLeod says to John Hagart, his assistant, on the Scotland bench. Ten minutes before half-time, Rioch is fouled inside the penalty area by Herbert Prohaska, an Austria forward desperately defending, and Archie Gemmill sweeps the spot-kick past Koncilia. One minute later, John Robertson, on Scotland's left wing, breaks past his man, quickly looks up and, with the Austrian defenders scampering back into position, takes advantage of their momentary disarray to sweep a long, curved pass into the path of Kenny Dalglish who, on the edge of the 'D', uses the top of his boot to lift the ball over Koncilia and into the net. 'I told you you were playing a bunch of nobodies,' MacLeod yells exuberantly as his players settle down in the dressing room at half-time.

As if to confirm MacLeod's words, a simple move, eight minutes after the break, rips the Austrian defence apart. Alan Rough's long goal-kick is taken down expertly by Joe

Jordan, who gallops past two defenders and into the Austrian penalty area, spreading enough confusion by the alacrity of his movement to leave Dalglish unmarked. When Jordan's reverse pass reaches Dalglish he has an easy job to stroke it into the net. Erich Obermayer's lucky lob over Rough gives the Austrians a goal ten minutes from time but before the end the Scots break speedily again and Jordan tees up Graeme Souness for a simple goal and the final flourish in a 5–1 win.

· 1978 · 1978 · 1978 · 1978 · 1978 · 1978 · 1978 · 1978 · 1978 · 1978 ·

A rollicking 2–2 draw with West Germany in their next match leaves the Scots needing only a point from their final group game, with Italy, to reach the final, although a victory for the Italians would see them into the final at Scotland's expense. It is a situation that leaves the Azzurri in something of a quandary. Facing Scotland, they would traditionally concentrate on defence and hitting on the break but, needing a win, the onus is more on the Italians to take the initiative. At the press conference prior to the match, MacLeod is asked about tactics.

'Well, that seems like a bit of a sugar-coated question to me,' he responds. 'After we played against Peru, I heard that one of you experts in the press had suggested that I thought tactics were a type of mint-flavoured sweet. So I'll leave it to you deep thinkers in the media to tell your readers all about the tactics that we will need to win this game.

'All I will say is that I'm having some emergency joinery work done to my house back in Ayr – it has got to be done

185

now, before my family fly out for the final. We are having a corner cabinet built – just big enough to display the World Cup trophy. I would also like to say, most sincerely, that from next year the twenty-fifth of June should be a national holiday in Scotland because you can mark down the twenty-fifth of June 1978 as the day Scottish football conquers the world. For on that Sunday I'm convinced the finest team this country has ever produced can play in the final of the World Cup in Buenos Aires and win. I give my permission here and now for the big celebration on the twenty-fifth of June to be made a national festival: a national Ally-day.'

· 1978 · 1978 · 1978 · 1978 · 1978 · 1978 · 1978 · 1978 · 1978 · 1978 ·

The match with Italy sees the Scots play in Buenos Aires for the first time in this tournament. The first serious piece of action sees Romeo Benetti, the Italy centre-back, sending Roberto Bettega coursing toward the Scotland goal. Stuart Kennedy races back to cover but as he goes to tackle Bettega, Rough converges on the two outfield players and the ball goes bobbling into the Scots' goal. The score remains 1–0 to the Italians at half-time, when MacLeod addresses his players. 'Can you imagine lifting the World Cup?' he asks them. 'It's like lifting your first child for the first time. You don't want to miss out on it. You just need to put in more effort in the second half and the game's yours. Now, don't let all the hard work you have put into this tournament so far be undone this afternoon. You've got forty-five minutes to make sure that doesn't happen.

'Now, down to business. I need some money from you. I want you all to go to your pockets and give me what you can because, do you know, that on the Italian bench they are taking bets on how many goals they are going to score in the second half? They are jumping around laughing and telling us it will be three, four, five, you know what they're like. So I want to give them some dough to put on us, just to even it up a bit – because they are not giving us a chance.'

The players look at MacLeod, dumbfounded. Eventually, Rioch, the captain, springs to his feet and says, 'Right, you heard the manager. I want you all to empty your pockets so that we can get a right good bet on.' Soon there is a flurry of activity as pesos pour into a small cloth bag produced by Hugh Allan, the physiotherapist. It takes the players' minds off their situation in the match and relaxes them with a bit of laughter so that as the time nears to re-enter the field, there is a freshness, resolve and degree of concentration among them to prove the Italians wrong. Limbering up before kick-off for the second half, the players' attention is drawn to the Italian bench, where MacLeod makes a great ceremonial show of handing over the sack of money to Enzo Bearzot, the bemused Italian coach who, along with the rest of the Italian bench, has no idea what this latest eccentric gesture from the Scotland manager is all about.

As expected, the Italians now sit back and pack their defence, leaving Bettega and Paolo Rossi, their two great striking talents, underemployed. It looks close to impossible for the Scots to get behind a deep-lying Italian side. For all MacLeod's exhortations at half-time, his team has lost impetus by the mid-point of the second period after finding that their efforts to break down the Italian defence have come to nothing. The manager realizes he will have to intervene again to spur on his team and, after a hefty foul on Jordan from Benetti that results in the striker receiving extensive treatment, MacLeod signals for Rioch and Dalglish to come over to the touchline. On the resumption of play, Dalglish drops deeper, as does Robertson, the winger, with Jordan still pushed up hard on the Italian back line. When a cross for Jordan is cleared by the Italian defence and drops to Dalglish, twenty yards from goal and at an angle, there are a dozen bodies between him and goal. His instantaneous lob uses those defenders as cover to blind Dino Zoff, the Italy goalkeeper, who looks like a bemused spectator searching the sky for a supersonic aircraft only to see it finally just as it passes above him in a blur; Zoff sights the ball only when it is streaking unassailably over him and into the top left-hand corner of his net.

The Italians need to score again but are slow to re-adjust to attacking mode and when Rioch receives the ball in midfield, just inside the Italian half, no one comes to meet him. The Scot advances, cutting diagonally infield. Still no Italian comes to him and when he gets to thirty-five yards from goal, he recalls quickly how Rough had told him of the difficulty for goalkeepers in dealing with the new, lightweight ball being used in this tournament, the Adidas Tango.

With Zoff drawn towards his near post Rioch bends over the ball, head down, almost in a crouching position, and lets fly a shot that whips across the Italian penalty area. Zoff leaps to his left but just when the goalkeeper looks to have it covered, the ball takes on a life of its own and veers off its previous path to elude Zoff's fingers, clip the inside of the post and finally settle inside the net on the other side of the goal. There are only ten minutes remaining of the semi but the life drains out of the Italians after this blow and Scotland defend their lead professionally until the final whistle, with which Angel Martinez, the Spanish referee, signals that they have reached the World Cup final.

There has never before been a World Cup like the one in Argentina. Every one of the host nation's matches is presided over by an untrustworthy-looking group of men – caricatures of movie-style gangsters: shifty-eyed, fidgety, oily, suspicious types in long overcoats. Shiftiest of all is General Jorge Videla, a wiry individual with a slicked-back parody of a military-man short-back-and-sides, who exudes nervousness despite being the all-powerful dictator of this temporarily benighted country. During matches, Videla constantly flicks furtive glances all around and chews cigarillos in the way a child gnaws on liquorice sticks. It is more than two years since his military junta seized power in Argentina and since then thousands of its political opponents, and innocent Argentinian citizens, have 'disappeared', presumed murdered. Long before Videla and his cronies assumed control of the country, the World Cup had been awarded to Argentina by FIFA and now Videla and his fellow generals opportunistically see Argentinian progress in the competition as a way of bolstering a regime that has suspended trial by jury and done away with civil liberties.

The arrival of Argentina in the final, and the accompanying public adulation, appears to have vindicated the junta's confidence in the reviving powers of the World Cup despite the team being managed by César Luis Menotti, whose political sensibilities appear at odds with the ringing right-wing proclamations of the junta. Menotti, a thirty-nine-year-old whose shoulder-length hair complements the flowing locks of his players, and who favours white suits and trendy, open-necked, party-going-playboy-style shirts, espouses 'left-wing football', which, he says expansively, is 'first of all, about scoring more goals than the opposition, but doing so through fluent attacking movements, waves of artistry that mirror the poetry of Borges, the prose of Ernesto Sábato and the music of Chick Corea'.

For all Menotti's cool and his expression of his cherished, alternative approach to life and work, it is understandably difficult for him to comment on the punitive regime that appears to have a cast-iron grip on his country. Privately, in advance of the contest with Scotland, he has told his players, 'When we enter the field on the day of the final, we have to look at the people in the stands. We are not going to look at the stage box of the authorities, we are going to look to the terraces, to all the people, where perhaps sits the father of each of us, because there we will find the metalworkers, the butchers, the bakers and the taxi drivers.' Such sentiments, if repeated in public, even from someone as high profile as Menotti, would be wildly dangerous in Argentina and so, of necessity, this urbane individual imposes self-censorship.

It is hard to imagine a gag, self-imposed or not, being placed on Ally MacLeod. The Scotland manager's conviction that his team will win the tournament could, he is aware, be construed as an insult to its hosts, who are now the only obstacle to him fulfilling what he sees as his destiny. Not one to shy away from further publicity, he decides to confront, head-on, the issue. Two days before the final, MacLeod takes his Scotland team for a stroll that leads them into the heart of Buenos Aires and to the national monument, a towering obelisk in the Plaza de la República that reaches, it seems, almost to the clouds. Following Argentina's 6–0 victory over Peru two days earlier, which saw the host nation into the final, thousands of celebrating Argentinians had thronged the plaza; and the ones with the greatest stamina had maintained wild revelry for the following thirty-six hours. Street-cleaners are removing the last of the resulting debris from around the obelisk as MacLeod and his players gather at its foot this Friday mid-morning. They crane their necks to peer upward at the Obelisco de Buenos Aires, this great symbol of Argentinian pride, constructed in the 1930s to celebrate the 400th anniversary of the founding of the city.

The press, as always, are in tow, as are radio reporters who are transmitting a live broadcast to the football-frenzied Argentinian nation. With Menotti and his men resting up after their win over the Peruvians, the focus is on the Scots today and MacLeod is happy to answer the obligatory questions about football before being asked by one journalist, from the *Buenos Aires Herald*, if his statement that Scotland are to be inevitably the world champions is not disrespectful to Argentina. MacLeod takes time to consider his reply, then says, 'Let me say first of all how wonderful the hospitality we have received from the Argentinian people has been.' There is recognition among the local press men that it looks clearly as though MacLeod has wisely opted to steer clear of potential controversy. 'They have,' continues the manager, 'been gracious, friendly, accommodating and have done so much to help us to enjoy our stay in this beautiful and extraordinary country.

'Now, let me turn your question around a bit; if not on its head. Would not a victory for Scotland be a victory for Argentina, too? Less of an insult than a blessing? So when I say that we must win I have the interests of the Argentinian people deep in my heart. Let's be honest, certain individuals would use an Argentinian victory for their own ends, wouldn't they? You all know whom I mean. And those ends would not exactly be beneficial for the Argentinian people, with bad effects that would linger long after the celebrations if Argentina were to win on Sunday night.

'I'm lucky that, as a foreigner, I am able to speak like this – at a time when, I know, Argentinian folk cannot talk freely. We have seen the mothers in the Plaza de Mayo lamenting the loss of their children, the disappeared ones, and it struck a chord with us. Maybe, sometimes, there are more important issues than football – and I say that as a football person through and through. So a victory for Scotland is a win for Argentina.'

There is utter astonishment among the Argentinian journalists present, notably because they know that these electrifying words are being broadcast via radio to millions of Argentinians who are in a state of frenzy two days in advance of the World Cup final. The transmission, they know, will be cut off quickly but too late for MacLeod's·words not to have resonated across the country.

· 1978 · 1978 · 1978 · 1978 · 1978 · 1978 · 1978 · 1978 · 1978 · 1978 ·

The following day, the *Buenos Aires Herald*, the city's English-language newspaper – founded by William Cathcart, a Scotsman – prudently fails to report MacLeod's words but it does react to them, obliquely, by asking the junta to issue lists of missing people, albeit balancing that comment by stating that people are happy that the 'red' terrorism that led to the introduction of the military regime has abated. 'Even so, and with approval for our government and its successes,' the article continues, 'we have to wonder why several billion pesos have been spent to stage the World Cup tournament in a country that is suffering from 186 per cent inflation.'

A jumpy junta has been unnerved by MacLeod's words, which are potentially a match to tinder. The generals respond by using the Argentinian press on the day of the final to issue an official statement, from General Videla, that reads:

> This is a day of great joy - Argentina in their second World Cup final, against Scotland, a nation with as fine a pedigree in international football as any other on earth but whose manager, Mr MacLeod, sometimes forgets to repay the gracious hospitality he has received in this our mother country.
> This will be a day of tremendous national celebration, of patriotism, when our players must show courage. It is a day for the people to show the world that life goes on as normal in Argentina and that, whatever incorrect stories may have been issued abroad, or believed by easily misled visitors to our shores, our country is unified in its desire for stability and order.

Another – junta-issued – statement also appears on all front pages of the newspapers along with that of Videla. The dispatch, whose author remains anonymous, tells readers:

> On this day of joy, it would be shameful if any irresponsible criminal or hooligan elements were to spoil the enjoyment of the occasion by the majority. And so the forces of defence of the country will be present to ensure that there is no disruption to the occasion. Colonel Senen Rozas, chief of the Buenos Aires Provincial Police, says, with due reasonableness, 'We will do all we need to do to maintain civil order – and we always try not to shoot'.

For all Menotti's fabled cool, he still displays a certain uneasiness about facing the Scots. Refereeing decisions have demonstrably gone Argentina's way throughout the tournament but, with the incorruptible Abraham Klein, an Israeli, as match official, they suffered a first-round defeat to the Italians that forced them to play their three second-round group games away from Buenos Aires and left them needing the hefty 6–0 victory over Peru to secure their place in the final. Klein is the only referee to have stood up fully to the Argentinians, correctly denying their plea for a penalty in their match against the Italians. More compliant referees have helped ease Argentina on their way to the final but the Argentinians' efforts to have a friendly referee appointed for the game with Scotland came to nothing when Artemio Franchi, their man inside FIFA, fell ill and the casting vote went instead to the Swede, Martin Aeki. He has gone with Klein, a selection that is a source of some relief to the Scots. 'I am sure all referees are fair,' Klein says in advance of the final, 'but not all are strong.'

'Right,' MacLeod tells his players as they await kick-off. 'Everyone in Scotland has been telling us how this team should play but I have refused to have anything or anyone from outside interfering. There were some problems for us all at the start of this tournament but look how well we have come together. You realized, as the finest group of players our country has ever produced, that you had to give everything at your disposal – and you have given it.

'I have known all along that you had the gifts to be a great team, even when others doubted you, and today is your chance to show how great this team can be. There will be no second chances after today. Think about that for a moment . . . This is it. After the World Cup, things are bound to change: there may be a new manager and perhaps some of you will move on and other players will come in; not one of you can be sure even of taking part in the World Cup in 1982, never mind winning it. So seize the moment. Noo's the day and noo's the hour. Get out there and win that World Cup!'

The players, believing MacLeod's pre-match address to be over, make their last-dash preparations around the dressing room, but soon notice that MacLeod, rather than darting around busily as is his wont, is standing stock-still and, gradually, the players understand that he is again seeking their attention. Now, with all eyes upon him, Ally, lithe and athletic even in middle age, springs into a handstand: as he does so, coins cascade from his trouser pockets, his wallet tumbles from inside his jacket and bank notes and team lines float to the floor; his watch unclasps and drops down to hang loose on his wrist; his tie flops over his face and his trousers flap at half-mast. Now, Scotland's manager delivers his final words of encouragement to the team, 'See how easy it is to turn everything upside down in an instant?' he says. 'Well, the world expects this Argentina team to seize victory tonight. It is up to you to turn the world on its head.'

· 1978 · 1978 · 1978 · 1978 · 1978 · 1978 · 1978 · 1978 · 1978 · 1978 ·

Outside the Monumental Stadium, the tangy, spicy smells of street vendors' choripanes and empanadas, sharpened in the chilly Buenos Aires winter air, suddenly become mingled with tear gas – and then cordite. A large number of Argentinian supporters' tickets for the section of the stadium behind one goal have proved to be counterfeit and hugely disappointed, angry and frustrated supporters are milling around outside the stadium in the minutes before kick-off. When Colonel Rozas's men attempt to move them away from the stadium – the only place they want to be today of all days – the fans, mixture of desperate disappointment, high excitement and pent-up anger becomes combustible and they resist the police. Tear gas is fired into the crowd by a nervy police force, placed on high alert by a junta now fearing dissent in the wake of Ally MacLeod's politically inflammatory radio broadcast from the Plaza de la República.

When being attacked with tear gas proves only to be more provocative to a crowd that has no intention of sloping away without protest at their exclusion from a World Cup final that they expected to attend without any complications, the police fire bullets. Three supporters – a teenage boy, his mother and a twenty-eight-year-old man – topple to the ground and, though their lifeless bodies are shovelled swiftly away by the security forces, fury sweeps through the few thousand supporters still straggling through the turnstiles, supporters whose emotions are now shredded by the anticipation of a great, unique, not-to-be missed football match and horror at what they have just witnessed.

News of the atrocity soon spreads throughout the terraces and, though over the past two years the Argentinian people have become used to hearing of outrages, the sullying of this great national occasion with casual brutality somehow seems a step too far. The fanatical chants of 'Ar-gen-ti-na! Ar-gen-ti-na!', repeated ad infinitum, in support of the team at matches previous to this one, is now directed with violent, vibrant force at the VIP box, where Videla and his cronies look more uncomfortable than ever, with considerable justification. The chant remains an expression of nationalism but it is now being used to tell Videla and Co. that they are the opposition, and that the nation is united against them. The junta have never needed an Argentinian victory on the football field more than they do now.

· 1978 · 1978 · 1978 · 1978 · 1978 · 1978 · 1978 · 1978 · 1978 · 1978 ·

Everyone thinks they know how Scotland play; that they are an open book, easy to read. Ernst Happel, the Holland manager, early in the tournament condescendingly described the Scots' style as, 'Still a bit kick and rush, though the players are strong and they seem to run for ever.' That Scots are predictable is a widely held view and when opposing teams see the tall, fearsome, front-teeth-free Joe Jordan line up in the Scotland attack, they immediately prepare for a direct aerial assault. This has worked hugely to the Scots' advantage in Argentina where Jordan, whose ball playing skills are underrated because of his toughness and his ability in the air, has often been allowed to run riot in and around the penalty area by defenders who have underestimated his talents. Jordan has thus been given the scope to work creatively in tandem with the bright, wily, inventive Dalglish. Similarly, opponents expect Scottish wingers to dart for the goal-line, sling over high crosses and do little else but in John Robertson, the Scots have a winger who bucks the stereotype; a player who habitually does almost everything else but hit the goal-line; instead, he will cross tellingly early from a deep position or thread a pass or chip cleverly in behind defenders for the strikers to chase.

The midfield players – Bruce Rioch, Asa Hartford and

Graeme Souness – are more traditionally in the Scottish mould: all three are determined ball winners who can mix the dirty work of asserting themselves with force and then using the ball with subtlety and delicacy; as if the former allows them licence to do the latter. It is a blend that few nations can replicate in their midfield players so why change something that works so well? With Sandy Jardine and Stuart Kennedy, the full-backs, supplementing the men in front of them and with Tom Forsyth and Martin Buchan, the centre-backs, similarly willing to join in attack when the time is right, this is a Scotland team that can take the opposition by surprise from all points on the pitch.

It is, indeed, with an element of surprise that the Scots begin the final match of the 1978 World Cup. MacLeod's greatest strength is as a motivator, a giver of belief, a man manager but he is also a keen and close observer of the game of football and is good at planting ideas in his players' minds; ideas that seem almost unimportant but that can unsettle and surprise the opposition.

The normal thing that footballers the world over do when taking the kick-off is for one of the two standing over the ball to play it backward to a midfield player; the unspoken understanding being that he has more time on the ball to think about what to do next, given that the opposition, restrained to their own half by the rules before the ball begins turning, have some distance to go before they can reach him.

The Scots now buck the trend. Jordan taps the ball to Dalglish and instead of knocking the ball backward, he takes it forward, surprising the two Argentinian strikers, whom he duly bypasses with ease. On he goes, twisting around Osvaldo Ardiles and then Daniel Passarella before threading the ball forward to the supporting Jordan as Daniel Bertoni closes in with a killer tackle. Jordan moves it wide to Robertson, who gives it back to Hartford. The midfield player, on the right side of the field, just outside the Argentinian penalty area, notes the Argentinians flooding back toward their own goal like lemmings and dinks a beautiful pass over their heads, to the back post, where Dalglish sprints to meet the ball and nod it over the outrushing Ubaldo Fillol, the Argentina goalkeeper. Less than a minute has passed of the 1978 World Cup final and Scotland are 1–0 ahead.

Only Fillol stands between Scotland and a landslide as he makes save after save in the subsequent minutes: from Rioch, Dalglish twice and Jordan. Souness bustles into the box and from eight yards shoots for the roof of the net but Fillol springs into the air and deflects it over the top. Stuart Kennedy cuts in from the right and Américo Gallego, the Argentina player, dives full length in an attempt to clear but instead sends the ball pelting furiously toward his own goal. Fillol stretches and uses both fists to smack it away. Tom Forsyth meets a corner on the six-yard line and Fillol turns the ball over the bar.

Argentina have barely managed to make it out of their own half but with fewer than ten minutes to go before half-time, Ardiles turns the ball on to Leopoldo Luque, who dances away from two challenges on the edge of the Scottish penalty area and nudges it to Mario Kempes who uses his left foot to drag the ball cleverly between Martin Buchan and Forsyth before whisking a left-footed shot under the body of Rough. The Argentinian crowd, which has been growing increasingly restless until this point, leap up in celebration, like 80,000 collectively popping champagne corks, and white ticker tape – a motif of this tournament – rains down from the highest of the stadium's many tiers.

The match is more even after half-time and though it is

also peppered increasingly by wild fouling from the Argentinians, the Scots are not intimidated. The fouls serve only as a reminder of the desperation of their opponents, who had felt the tournament was theirs to win by right and are worried that if they cannot win their first World Cup now, on home ground, they may never begin to emulate the tremendous World Cup pedigree of their great Brazilian rivals. The almost entirely Argentinian crowd – only 500 or so Scots have made the expensive and daunting journey to South America – feel more and more nervous with each passing minute and this is transmitted to the field. With two minutes remaining, Menotti rises from the dugout, darts to the touchline and, in an effort to revive his faltering team, yells at the players nearest him, 'Hey, there are eighty thousand of us and only eleven of them – we cannot lose this!'

The Argentina manager is still on his feet when another wild tackle sees Passarella send Rioch crashing to the ground, just inside the Scottish half. As Souness moves to take the kick, Bertoni crowds him. Kempes and Luque wait on their toes behind Souness, anticipating a block from one of their team-mates to set up a scoring chance, but Souness, the option of a short pass cut off by the blocking of Bertoni, decides to hit the ball long and it curls from right to left, all the way to the Argentinian penalty box, where Jorge Olguin, the right-back, gets caught under it. Fillol races from his line but it is his first miscalculation of the day because Jordan gets to the ball well before him and sends it under the flying goalkeeper's body. There is only medium power on the striker's shot and as it rolls forward it looks as though it is most likely to strike the post. Instead, it squirts just inside the upright. Jordan is mobbed by his team-mates as the entire Argentinian team rushes to the referee, trying to persuade Mr Klein, by sheer weight of numbers, that there is merit in their protest and that there has been an infringement in the scoring of the goal. Klein refuses to be moved and points to the centre circle.

A weaker referee would play some unmerited minutes of additional time to try to assuage the Argentinians but Mr Klein allows only the remaining twenty-five seconds to expire before blowing his whistle.

Scotland are world champions for a second time but their victory is greeted in near silence as their few supporters, dotted around the crowd, cannot make any significant amount of noise. The Argentinian players stand still as statues and the crowd remain stock still in a state of shock for several minutes while the Scots players and MacLeod cavort on the field in joy. Videla waits to carry out his prescribed duty of presenting the trophy, a matter uncomfortable to him now that he will not be using the moment for propaganda purposes. Finally, the Argentinian crowd finds its collective voice again and a great roar of furious, bottled-up hatred engulfs the Monumental Stadium. It is as if, in the vacuum left by defeat, they recognize how empty a regime-backed victory for Argentina would have been. The stadium has become a tinderbox. This is not about football now. This is a turning of the tables on the men who have tried to use the Argentinian people's love of football for their own ends.

One young man, a blue and white hat perched on his head, leaps over a wall that separates Videla and his men from the crowd. A soldier darts toward the intruder and, rather than shoot him in full view of the crowd, smashes the butt of his rifle down into the man's face, bloodying the national colours on the man's hat. The soldier's violence incenses the crowd and Videla stands frozen as half a dozen more individuals, undaunted by the fate of their predecessor, encroach on his eyrie. This now makes for a struggle with his guards rather than a straightforward repulsion. More and more angry fans surge forward until the soldiers guarding the dictator finally give up and retreat. Videla makes a quick exit but he is pursued vigorously by the throng – he is unlikely to get very far.

This is not the only part of the stadium in which the people have risen up against the regime. The field of play is now invaded by Argentinian supporters, military security wisely withholding their batons, and they dart forward to MacLeod, grabbing him and raising him shoulder-high to lead him on a victory lap of the perimeter of the pitch, his players following him, as they receive tumultuous applause from the thousands still on the terraces. Back on the turf at the end of his exalted progress around the field, MacLeod makes a beeline for Menotti, standing just inside his dugout, smoking, with an air of philosophical resignation. Ally exhorts his Argentinian oppo to come out and on to the edge of the pitch, where MacLeod raises Menotti's arm to the sky.

The Argentinian players now lift Menotti onto their shoulders and he, too, is taken around on a lap of honour at the end of which he motions to an aide, who disappears down the players' tunnel and reappears with the World Cup trophy, which Menotti, in one of the great iconic, photographic moments of the 20th century, presents to MacLeod and the Scottish players. Scotland have won the World Cup but this has been an immortal joint victory for fun and freedom.

THE STEIN SCENE

'Picking the team now, are you, eh? Picking the team?' Jimmy Mallick, a prominent Scottish sports reporter, looks up to find the unmistakable source of these words, the bulky figure of Jock Stein, looming over him and when Stein, the Scotland manager, homes in on someone to put them right on some matter or other, he seems to grow taller and more intimidating the longer the dressing-down lasts. Mallick, labelled the 'voice of Scottish football' by his newspaper, had been fiddling with the straps on his suitcase before checking it in for the flight to Spain and the 1982 World Cup and now, confronted by a fractious Stein, he knows that he has little option but to take the abuse.

Mallick's 'crime' has been to suggest in his morning column that Willie Miller should be partnered by Alex McLeish, Miller's

Aberdeen team-mate, in Scotland's central defence, rather than by Alan Hansen, the Liverpool defender. 'Hansen and Miller do not a good partnership make,' opined Mallick in his direct style that brooks no contradiction. 'It is like putting tomato sauce on your cornflakes at the breakfast table this good morning – it just does not go.' This is the cause of Stein's irritation and as the rest of Mallick's travelling journalist colleagues look on, some in silent pleasure but others uncomfortably aware it could be them next, Stein forcefully bypasses the letters page to voice his emphatic response to Mallick's piece.

'So when did you become a football expert?' Stein asks the 'voice of Scottish football', glowering down on the reporter, who remains crouched beside his suitcase, unwilling to stand up for fear of further provoking the heavily-built Stein, still a fearsome figure even in his late-fifties. 'Think you can choose my team for me, do you? Listen, you could put what you know about football on the back of a stamp and still have room for a shopping list. I wouldn't ask for your advice on how to make a cup of tea, never mind football. Writer? You couldnae write home to mother. Don't put anything else in your paper about who should or shouldn't be in my team, right. I pick this team. You do your wee stories.' With a look of distaste for the reporter, Stein turns and walks across the concourse to rejoin the main body of the squad, leaving Mallick to pick at his wounds.

· 1982 · 1982 · 1982 · 1982 · 1982 · 1982 · 1982 · 1982 · 1982 · 1982 ·

There is a certain tension in being world champions and Jock Stein, hypersensitive to every nuance, every ebb and flow of fortune in the football world, is hugely aware of that. This has put him in a most prickly mood as he embarks upon his latest World Cup adventure. The defending champions at every World Cup are treated as something of a curiosity: they are given a degree of respect for their past achievement but everyone knows that that was four years ago and that they have qualified without becoming battle-hardened by a qualifying competition. While other nations have criss-crossed their respective continents to achieve success in the qualifying stages, the world champions instead have been smoothing their way through a series of friendly matches. The list of champions to have successfully defended their crown is, consequently, not a long one. All of these factors mean that everyone else is subconsciously preparing for Scotland's downfall.

Stein is aware of how quickly hard-earned reputations can be tarnished — after years of enormous success at Celtic he left the club on a low after only one particularly poor season. That was in 1978 and although Stein could have subsequently forged a lucrative career in English football, the desire of Jean, his wife, to remain in Scotland has meant that the only real option for him was the post of national team manager. This became vacant when Ally MacLeod, mastermind of the 1978 World Cup triumph, was elected as president of the new Scottish Parliament following the 1979 vote in favour of devolution that became a landslide victory, owing almost entirely to the nation's euphoria at the success of the national team in Argentina and the personal charisma of MacLeod after he had been persuaded to lead the political campaign.

The down-to-earth style of Stein is entirely different to that of MacLeod. A less voluble approach is Stein's preferred method for tackling the vagaries of football and he attends to every behind-the-scenes detail so that the business of playing football can go as smoothly as possible: this includes seemingly minor matters that he expects will count for a lot, such as ensuring that several chests of tea bags be shipped out from the UK to Spain during the tournament to make his men feel more at home.

Stein's ethos contrasts severely with the broad brush strokes favoured by MacLeod, who has spent the past three years jetting around the world, using his extra-extrovert personality to drum up business for Scotland and to put forward the case for full independence. Only occasionally, nowadays, will MacLeod let loose on the subject of football, such as when, two months prior to this World Cup he has blithely heaped enormous pressure on Stein and his team by stating, 'Och, there can be few things as important to us all as a nation than winning that last World Cup, unless it is winning it again – and this time they only need to hop across the water to Spain to bring it back. We had to go to the other side of the world and take the trophy with an entire military dictatorship on our backs. So, this time it should be easy and if Scotland win the World Cup I am sure it will be a boost not just to trade but in our bid to win a majority in our referendum on full independence for Scotland, which, I can exclusively reveal, will be held on Thursday 15 July, just four days after the World Cup final in Madrid. '

· 1982 · 1982 · 1982 · 1982 · 1982 · 1982 · 1982 · 1982 · 1982 · 1982 ·

Now that he is out in Spain, Stein feels he can at last relax to some degree, having left MacLeod and all his works well behind, but there is a degree of tetchiness around the Scotland party and Stein feels it keenly. Everyone wants to knock the World Cup holders off their perch and with the Scotland players having earned good money and a high profile world-wide since winning the trophy in 1978, they are no longer seen as a gallant, plucky little country, merrily upsetting the favourites. This change in attitude toward the Scots is compounded by the prospect of Scotland winning independence and, as has been widely reported, blossoming into one of the richest small countries in the world, thanks to revenues from North Sea oil. Prior to the tournament's opening match, at the Nou Camp in Barcelona – which, as tradition dictates, features the holders – Guy Thys, the Belgium manager, turns up the heat even higher by declaring, 'We are playing the world champions but we are not facing the best team in the world.'

· 1982 · 1982 · 1982 · 1982 · 1982 · 1982 · 1982 · 1982 · 1982 · 1982 ·

Jimmy Mallick wearily climbs the steps to the press box, high inside the multi-tiered Nou Camp stadium. A round-faced man with scraggy, greying hair, rheumy eyes that float in their sockets like the yolks of poached eggs, and lips that remain tightly pursed – even when he speaks he opens only one side of his mouth and then seemingly grudgingly. He is carrying a long, canvas bag and has the slightly furtive overall demeanour of a night-burglar setting off on his rounds, despite being dressed bohemian-smart in a silver checked suit with a thin cravat tied around his scrawny throat. He finds big Al Davis, a pal from the Scottish press, who shifts one seat along to make way for Mallick.

'I would love to be responsible for that big bandit's obituary,' Mallick mutters and Davis immediately knows he is referring to the manager. 'What are you going to do?' he responds. 'Bludgeon him to death with your ballpoint? Look, we all know that you don't mess with Stein. You were just unlucky that he happened to find you on the morning you'd written something about him. Could have been any one of us.'

'I know,' Mallick says, 'but what I mean is, I want to be able to write the report that makes Stein yesterday's man. He was good in the past but has he still got it? I mean, look how quickly Celtic got shot of him. Does that not tell you something? Then he's been in this job four years, he's missed out on the European Championships and Scotland didn't have to qualify for this tournament. So what's he done? Nothing – a big fat zero. That's a grand total of zilch in five years. So how I'd like it if he fell flat on his face in this game tonight. How I would love to stick the knife right in.'

'Hey, hey, wait a minute, Jimmy,' Davis says. The latter is a lanky individual with a mess of black curls atop his head and an unnaturally red-raw complexion, as if his skin had been turned inside out and scrubbed hard; either that or pickled in alcohol. 'Do you realize what you're saying? You want Scotland to lose so that you can write something bad about Stein? This is Scotland we're talking about here – in the World Cup.'

'Ach,' Mallick replies, scoring hard on a notepad with a well-chewed ballpoint that is producing no ink at all. 'For me, seeing that big so-and-so lose would be the best result we could get tonight. Anyway, we've had plenty success in the past and it cannae last for ever. And I'll be here all the way to the final anyway no matter who gets through to the next stage.'

The lengthy World Cup opening ceremony draws to a close with flamenco dancers whirling and twirling before a dove flutters into the sky, released from inside a football by a young boy in the strip of the Spanish national team. Mallick, who has sat head down throughout the ceremony, using the press box telephone to natter away to people back home, comes off the telephone and finally raises his head to look at the pitch on which the boy is now there on his own, the hundreds of other participants in the ceremony having retreated. 'That it, eh?' Mallick moans to Davis. 'I thought this opening ceremony of theirs was supposed to be some sort of a big production number. Instead, you get one wee boy in a fitba' strip?'

Mallick settles down in the hope of seeing Stein and Scotland come a cropper but the match is a stodgy struggle, the Belgians sitting back and Stein's Scotland reluctant to commit too much to attack. Half-time arrives with neither side having created much, Scotland's only serious effort on goal a free-kick from John Robertson that clears the Belgian defensive wall and dips down under the crossbar, where it is clutched safely by Jean-Marie Pfaff. 'So much for Stein's brave new world,' Mallick mutters as the teams troop in for half-time.

Bocadillos and beer, gratis inside the press room, cheer Mallick at the interval. After the break the match becomes more open and midway through the second half, Erwin Vandenbergh finds himself free when the ball is played neatly to him in behind the Scottish defence. He looks offside, he feels offside, as evidenced by him taking several glances at the linesman and then dilly-dallying on the ball as if awaiting the referee's whistle. It does not come and the midfield player, eventually, decides to proceed, curving a twenty-yard left-footed shot around Alan Rough, the Scotland goalkeeper.

Up in the press box, Mallick smiles, albeit maliciously, with the ends of his lips turned down in a fashion that would be unsettling to anyone who might be looking. Mallick mutters contentedly to Davis, 'Time for me to get going on that obituary, I think.' Around him, he sees familiar Scottish colleagues assiduously keeping up with the game in best professional manner: one youngster, dyed-blond streaks in his hair, has a telephone clasped to his ear, through which he is maintaining a keen conversation with his fiancée; another is perusing the pages of a glossy Spanish gossip magazine.

Stein, now a heftier figure than in his prime a dozen or so years earlier, makes his way to the side of the pitch. His movements are slow and heavy as he raises his thick arms to point here and there around the field. The Iberian heat appears to have had the effect of slowing him down even further. It is difficult to know whether the players are taking any notice of him but, when the ball goes dead for Franky Vercauteren, the Belgium player, to receive some treatment, Stein calls over Graeme Souness, his captain, for a quick word. On the match's resumption, trained observers of the game can see that David Narey has been pushed forward into midfield: Stein has noted that the Belgians are playing everything through the middle so has gambled that he can do without a right-back for the closing stages.

After this, the Belgians are struggling to remain in the game, and when Scotland are awarded a free-kick on the edge of the penalty area Stein comes alive – briefly looking like the ghost of his younger self – frantically signalling to Gordon Strachan and John Robertson. Message received, the two Scots stand behind the ball, leaving the Belgians unsure which one of them will take the kick. On the referee's whistle, both potential takers dart towards the ball only to stop just short of it, glaring and gesticulating at each other, Laurel and Hardy fashion, as if to signify this has been a comically clownish moment of misunderstanding. It has not. With the Belgians relaxing as they watch the show unfold, Robertson, from a standing position, chips the ball up and over the wall and past a stationary Pfaff, who is thoroughly taken by surprise. The Belgians are so taken aback they fail to muster even a token protest, that staple of top-level football, to the Czech referee and the goal stands.

Every member of the Scotland team senses the energizing effect of equalizing and with eight minutes remaining, the Belgians are still metaphorically on their heels; literally too, when Strachan collects the ball on the halfway line and darts infield, past one man, two, then a third, before veering out to the wing and clipping a pass inside to Kenny Dalglish, who instantaneously whips the ball behind the unravelled Belgian defence and to the back post for John Wark to slide the ball into the net from close range.

'Rumours of Jock Stein's demise have proven to be greatly exaggerated,' Davis says drily as the final whistle goes. 'Oh, I'm looking forward to a nice, cool *cerveza* and to hearing big Jock explain how he got it right – again,' he adds laughingly as he rises and heads for the post-match press conference. Through working for an evening newspaper, Davis has the luxury of knowing that his report on the match is not due to be filed until the following morning. Mallick, in contrast, is faced with a late, hair-tearing rewrite of his initial story and, now, with Scotland's win, he knows that he can be only mildly critical, if critical at all, of the manager. It's not exactly a rewrite as such: Mallick is proud that he never writes a word of his reports; instead, equipped with an armoury of stock clichés, he dictates them off the top of his head to a copytaker. 'I reported the entire Moscow Olympics without touching a pen or a typewriter,' is one of his favourite boasts.

He does not believe in preparation; preferring to do things off the cuff. 'Keeps me fresh,' he will tell any colleague willing to listen, 'Keeps me fresh!' So, before the Scots' equalizer, convinced that they were going to lose, he had dictated a report back to Glasgow crucifying Stein for what Mallick describes as his tactical naivety and lack of imagination. Having sent over the bulk of his report early, Mallick had figured that he would top and tail it quickly so that his way would be free to avail himself of the best of the excellent refreshments provided for the fourth estate. Now he has to telephone his newspaper urgently and completely revise his story and he knows that by the time he has finished, the gannets among his associates will have polished off the buffet good and proper. 'Scotland had us all on tenterhooks up until the last moments of this match,' he begins his revised report in a depressed tone, once he has the copytaker on the line, 'leaving it desperately late, almost until the death, before snatching the win . . .'

· 1982 · 1982 · 1982 ·1982 · 1982 · 1982 · 1982 · 1982 · 1982 · 1982 ·

Victories over Hungary and El Salvador clinch Scotland's place in the second round and on the morning after the team's third win, Stein, a light sleeper even in the least exciting of times, is up at dawn and leaves the team's hotel to take a walk by himself through the village of Altea and down on to the beach. He takes a careful look to make sure there is no one around before quickly divesting himself of his clothes and throwing himself into the water. Soon, he is cavorting in the early morning surf, like a great bear suddenly thrown into surprisingly fluid gymnastic contortions; arms, legs, feet and head freely flail around as Stein fully lets himself go for the first time in weeks. It is a wonderful moment of release – he feels that he can finally relax fully, having seen the team into the next, more serious stage of the competition. He has proved, not least to himself, that he is no football dinosaur. So pleased is he that he decides to give the players a day off and, moreover, that he will venture into Alicante to pay a surprise visit to some of the 20,000 Scotland supporters who have travelled to Spain in support of the team. Many of them are reported to be eking out a most basic subsistence at the World Cup, sleeping on the beach, imbibing cheap wine and reportedly selling their blood to local clinics for £5 a time.

It is a bubbly Stein who is full of good cheer at breakfast, handing out spending money to his backroom staff and telling them to avail themselves of the hotel's facilities for the day and to pamper themselves as much as they please with massages and Jacuzzis. He informs the players of their leisure time, saying, 'I'll be away from the hotel until dinner time so if any of you are wanting a drink – and I don't suppose any of you are – but if any of you are wanting a quiet beer or two, I won't be asking any questions when I get back; as long as behaviour remains within the type of limits you know that I would expect.' Stein then has a quiet word with Graeme Souness, his captain, and with Kenny Dalglish, to reinforce his message that matters must not become too rowdy. With that, he repairs to his room, makes a cheery phone call home and then books a taxi to get him into Alicante later that morning.

When Stein arrives at that resort's seafront, he finds only

a few groups of fans, bleary-eyed from celebrating qualification the night before and unable quite to believe that the great Stein has come among them. As he takes the time to chat to them at length, in general terms, about the matches, more and more supporters are attracted to the hubbub and within half an hour the beach is crammed with Scots and curious Spanish onlookers. These are his fans now, Stein feels, they are no longer Ally's.

'Now remember,' he says, drawing himself up to his full height and looking as statesmanlike as possible, 'if the team does well and there are stories of our fans misbehaving, the world will sneer at us. I have been very proud of the way you have been conducting yourselves so far. It is a record to be pleased with that not one of you has been in trouble with the police. So let's keep it that way.'

A round of restrained applause ripples from the assembled fans and Stein continues dispensing his nuggets of footballing wisdom, 'John Robertson can turn a 4–4–2 into a 4–3–3 because of his skill, he is a brainbox on the field because of his coolness.

'Wouldn't it be great to play a match in the Bernabeu – that's the opera house of football; without Caruso, of course.' This draws a bit of a blank from the fans, predominantly in their late teens and early twenties, and more familiar with the warblers of Haircut 100 and Duran Duran.

'Anyway,' Stein continues, deciding that even mentioning the venue for the final was an incautious step too far, 'there are a lot of hard games to go before we can even think about the final.' This draws a lukewarm murmur of agreement from his audience.

'You know,' Stein adds, feeling he has to remind them of the checks and balances involved in top-level football, 'it shouldn't ever really be imaginable that we could win the World Cup. It should be almost impossible for a country our size; a dream.' Again, his words don't do a lot to stir the supporters and Stein is wondering whether he has lost his touch and what he can do to regain it, when he loses their attention for good.

All eyes are raised to look at a light aeroplane that comes flitting across the bay, bagpipe music blaring from speakers fixed underneath its wings and a long, white banner trailing from its fuselage, inscribed on one side with the words 'Scots Wha Hae' and on the other 'World Champions 1978 – Winners To Be 1982'. This brings from the fans the rousing cheer that Stein had been seeking but even that is subsumed by the sheer delirium that greets the next piece of seaside action. From around the corner of the cove a speedboat emerges, pulling after it a rubber ring in which stands, balanced acrobatically, none other than Ally MacLeod, kitted out in a wetsuit, Saltire in the hand that holds onto the rope that connects him to the boat, a Lion Rampant in the other hand, with which he also punches the air repeatedly.

The supporters sweep toward the shoreline, letting out a gigantic roar of approval and the boat turns to allow Ally to make another glide-by killing. It is when the boat is about to start its third journey across the bay that Stein gives up, realizing he simply cannot compete with this degree of showmanship, and goes in search of a taxi to return him to Altea and the relative sanity of the team hotel. Stein feels like a man who has come home to find his house locked and shuttered against him – and he wonders whether he will ever be able to find the key again.

Stein's mood is not lightened when he picks up a Scottish tabloid newspaper the following morning. 'Today's edition, rushed out to Spain so that the Scotland fans and players can read the latest with their hot morning rolls!' reads the excited blurb across the top of the front page. Mallick's latest story jumps out at Stein like a drunk seeking a scrap at closing time:

> Pelé and I travelled together from Madrid to
> Barcelona yesterday and the Brazilian great was
> in tremendous form, as always. 'Ah, Scotland I
> remember well, Scotland I love,' he told me. 'Do
> you know I once wore a kilt for some fun? Scotland
> are welcome at the World Cup but they won't win
> it.' So there you have it; in the words of a
> legend. Stein's team will unfortunately fall short.
> Pelé won't be taking in the Scots' matches in
> Barcelona – he will be at the glamour-group
> matches involving his beloved Brazil, plus
> Argentina and Italy on the other side of the city.
> In the eyes of the world, a group involving
> Scotland, Poland and the Russians isn't quite as
> attractive but it's what we've got and we'll have
> to make the most of it even if Stein's Scotland
> hasn't quite caught fire in this World Cup in the
> way that we would have liked.
> I also chatted to good comrade Beskov, the manager
> of the Russia team. He said he wasn't confident
> but then deception comes naturally to a Russian –
> note how the Russians are content to live in a
> hotel for decadent Westerners and they look far
> from unhappy clinking drinks at the side of a
> swimming pool surrounded by topless holidaymakers.
> When you throw in a Polish team that have reached
> the latter stages of the past two World Cups you
> have to wonder whether Stein and his team are
> about to falter and let down a nation – and its

undisputed leader Ally MacLeod – and fail to
retain the World Cup that was won in such glorious
style four years ago.

Stein throws aside the newspaper. These are the lonely
moments that make him wonder whether it is worth continuing as a manager. The sound of the crowd and the vibrancy
of training sessions have a galvanizing effect on him but now,
alone in yet another hotel room, with a cooling cup of tea, he
feels a sense of deflation. He realizes that reporters and
supporters will never understand the game the way he does
but he wonders if he is losing the will to play the public relations game that convinces supporters he is on their side and
that ensures he has their backing when times get tough. He
also wonders for how long he can remain in touch with the
players. Here in Spain, living cheek by jowl with the footballers of the eighties for a lengthy period of time, he is seeing
things that are almost beyond his ken. One player has a gold
ankle chain; another visits the hotel's hairdresser every afternoon after training to have his hair washed and blow-dried
just-so. Steve Archibald insists on smoked salmon before every
meal; Alan Rough, the languid goalkeeper from modest Partick
Thistle, ordered lobster bisque for dinner last night. To Stein,
the tough former miner, these modes of behaviour are puzzling
but as the international manager he does not have the power
to whip these players, financially independent of him, into
line the way he could at a club. He has to bite his tongue, he
feels, more often than is healthy for him.

The high-summer heat in Spain is taking its toll on him, too,
and he feels weary as he starts to pack his case for the switch
of venue up the coast to Barcelona for the second-round group
stage. The very act of preparing for the future, even in such
a minor fashion, cheers him, though, and he feels his strength

returning – once again there courses through him the desire to prove them all wrong, mingled with the anticipation of participating in another key game and with it the need to tune the players to perfection. *'Andiamo!'* he says to himself, bustling around the room and clapping his hands together. *'Andiamo!'*

· 1982 · 1982 · 1982 · 1982 · 1982 · 1982 · 1982 · 1982 · 1982 · 1982 ·

Just as there are those who are now prepared to question Stein, so there are onlookers who wonder whether Kenny Dalglish, also, is bobbing along too heavily reliant on a highly inflated reputation. The striker is, even after all these years in the team, still too subtle for most Scottish supporters, who look to see their forwards bash the ball into the net rather than appreciate the way Dalglish drops off to make space for others and to play passes for team-mates. Equally, the clever runs that he makes are sometimes simply not noticed by his less progressive colleagues.

Against the Poles in Barcelona, those seeking evidence of Dalglish's decline – he is now thirty-one years old – leave the Nou Camp with an answer in full. Five minutes have passed when Jordan plays the ball across the face of the goal and Dalglish leaps to nick a natty header over Józef Mlynarczyk, the Poland goalkeeper. Midway through the first half, Dalglish receives the ball just inside the Polish half and advances before stopping suddenly when he is twenty yards from goal. With half a dozen Polish defenders still rushing towards their own goal to cover, their bodies betray them by continued backward motion as Dalglish, now almost standing still, uses the split-second release gained by his surprise manoeuvre to dig the ball up and over Mlynarczyk and into the top corner. Three minutes after half-time, he cuts in from the goal-line and makes as if to shoot with his right foot but instead drags the ball onto his left boot as a defender dives full-length to try to block. A second defender goes to challenge Dalglish as he again looks ready to shoot but for a second time he eliminates his opponent by easing the ball farther to his left before instantaneously flighting the ball around the goalkeeper and into the welcoming stretch of netting between stanchion and post on the far side of goal. The 3–0 win leaves Scotland on the cusp of the semi-finals.

At the Nogano Hotel, later on the evening of the Poland game, Jimmy Mallick, already in a state of some irritation, is infuriated further by seeing new, temporary price stickers plastered on the drinks bottles behind the bar – a special welcome for the embedded Scottish press. It jars with him particularly because, while his colleagues are on expenses and can shrug off with a laugh the raised prices, he is having to pay his own way, having had his wings clipped after going out of bounds with an expenses claim for several thousand pounds for an evening in Madrid, pre-tournament, when he generously offered to host a dinner for colleagues. Weary from travel and then further incapacitated by drink, however, Mallick spent much of that evening slumped senseless in a corner while a horde of fellow press men and accumulated hangers-on helped themselves merrily to doubles and trebles on his tab, making the most of Spanish licensing laws that allow an establishment to remain open until the early hours. The following morning, Mallick had awoken groggily to discover the bill stuffed in the top pocket of his jacket together with a frightening receipt for his American Express card; a scraggy signature from him making official the horror of it all.

The increased bar prices are not his only grouse. His aeroplane flight to Bareclona was a rarity; he has had to spend June criss-crossing Spain by slow-moving train after slow-moving train, in stifling heat, to cover, daily, matches for his newspaper. Tired and frazzled, he arrived in the lounge bar this evening to find the sports editor of a London-based national Sunday newspaper trooping down from a room upstairs to order a sumptuous plate of sandwiches, tea, beer and cakes for the refreshment of Hughie McElfarry, that paper's star sports writer. When Mallick asked the sports editor, while the latter was awaiting the tray, why he was behaving in such servile fashion the response was that the scribe in question could not be disturbed. 'I can't do anything that would disturb Hughie while he is composing . . .' were the man's very words. It is the last straw for Mallick, who would kill for the luxury of putting together at his leisure nothing more than a couple of well-considered features each week – and his general disillusionment with being at a World Cup beset by accreditation problems and other haphazard moments of maladministration forms the basis of his next story, which is more like one long, lazy moan than sustained criticism. His complaints sound a jarring note with a Scottish populace who would love to be at the tournament and his sports editor informs him with a brisk and brief telephone call that better material is expected from him in the days ahead.

The press conference with Stein the following day provides Mallick with an opportunity for a more incisive story. When Stein is asked by a reporter about how important the Scottish fans are to the team's performance, the manager replies, 'Our fans are tremendous and they have made us proud with their behaviour but I have yet to see a fan score a goal. It's what we do on the field of play that's important.'

Mallick, seething at Stein's success in taking Scotland to the verge of the semi-finals, the dressing down the manager gave him at the airport and his compounded misfortunes since, quickly asks, 'Isn't that a bit disrespectful to our great supporters?' Stein takes stock, aware that the busy conference is populated by reporters from other countries and that he must be restrained in dealing with this loaded question. 'No,' he says after a brief pause. 'It is not disrespectful. The supporters are here to have fun and to cheer on the team, which they've been doing very well. We appreciate the amount of money they have spent in getting here and how important the whole enterprise is to them.

'I'll tell you what is disrespectful to the supporters: writing terrible stories and then having them sent out here hot-foot for our fans to read. You said the other day that you'd spoken to Pelé. Well I asked him about that at a reception last night and he can't remember that at all; funny that, since you said he had accompanied you all the way on your journey from Madrid to Barcelona.

'You said before the tourney that Jim Leighton would be capped for the first time in the friendly against the village team from Torralta that we played when we were in Portugal. How could anyone believe that a player would be capped for playing in a bounce game? You keep talking about Russia but it is actually called the Soviet Union – but that's only been for about sixty years so you maybe need more time to get up to date than that. So, you see, your stories are just riddled with mistakes and that's even before you begin writing your match reports.

'You said that we gave Poland too much room and were lucky to be saved by Dalglish. That's funny, because the Poland captain said after the match how every time he received the ball he would look up to find there were six or seven Scotland players running at him and that it was completely unnerving. Still, I suppose he's only on the pitch and you get a better view from up there in the press box, especially after you've had a few beers. I could go on about you and your mistakes but we would be here all night and I'm sure there are other people here who are ready to ask me some intelligent questions.'

The discomfort that Mallick feels at all this is compounded when, the following day, Scotland's press and players watch the Poles draw with the Soviet Union. Scotland, consequently, require only one point to qualify for the semis and they duly obtain it with a stuffy 0–0 draw against the Soviets. It means that their last roadblock en route to the final will be Italy.

· 1982 · 1982 · 1982 · 1982 · 1982 · 1982 · 1982 · 1982 · 1982 · 1982 ·

There is a certain serendipity that attaches itself to a team that has travelled far in a World Cup. Those who have previously questioned the team selection, tactics and approach, be they players, the more obstreperous members of the press, FA officials, old pros with biting opinions or dissatisfied supporters – quell their voices in recognition of the feat that has, unarguably, been achieved. Thus it is as Scotland prepare to play in the semi-final. Even dissenters such as Mallick, while not quite becoming fans of Stein, realize that further criticism will look like the rantings of a madman when set against the hard fact that the team has been brought to the brink of success. Those players who have felt slighted at being left out of the team put their irritation with the manager to one side for fear that any momentary flare-up of anger now could deprive them of a place in a history-making team, should injury or suspension to a squad-mate open up a place in the starting eleven for them. Supporters who have complained about the presence of this player or that player, this tactic or that tactic, while perhaps still unwilling to admit they were wrong, realize that their voice is now needed not for dissent but to help push the team on to glory.

Stein revels in the ultra-relaxed mood that this glowing feeling of unity brings to his squad. When Alan Rough awakens on the morning before the semi with the Italians, he finds he is sharing his bed with a horse's head; the sheets around it stained red. The ultra-relaxed Rough merely turns over and goes back to sleep, appearing at breakfast with the horse's head under his arm. 'That must have taken a lot of strawberry jam,' he announces to his assembled team-mates, and quickly drawing from Alan Brazil and John Wark the admission that they had dismembered the head of a rocking-horse they had picked up from a local toyshop. A waiter delivers a gilt-edged invitation to Stein bearing the legend, 'You are invited to be "godfather" at the forthcoming christening of Italy as World Cup also-rans'. Stein chuckles. 'I don't need to ask who did this,' he says. In fact, he has no idea who the perpetrator might be but he likes to spread the belief that he is an all-seeing, all-knowing presence; a ploy that works well with football players.

· 1982 · 1982 · 1982 · 1982 · 1982 · 1982 · 1982 · 1982 · 1982 · 1982 ·

Reality comes rushing at us as if fired down the barrel of a revolver and it seems as though Scotland have no sooner qualified for the last four and revelled in that success before the afternoon of the semi is upon them. It is a jocular party that heads for Barcelona's Nou Camp stadium, players stripped to the waist on the coach for temporary relief against the searing heat and Stein a jolly, burly figure in the front seat, chatting away happily to Jim McLean, his assistant.

While Stein has merrily maintained a relaxed front to keep the players gently primed for action, he and McLean have toyed tortuously with the problem of which type of team to field against the Italians. Their semi-final opponents have earned some notoriety for the manner in which they have reached this stage via sometimes brutal battles with Brazil and Argentina, so Stein has wondered often in the past forty-eight hours whether he should field a team with the inbuilt capability of waging war. Or will the Azzurri play to the positive talents of their darting, dashing, highly talented midfield players and forwards? Or will they, in traditional style, sit back and defend?

The Scotland manager is still puzzling over this problem, and has still not decided on his team, one hour prior to kick-off. Naming the team late, he has found, keeps every player on his toes. There seem to be few concerns from the Italian quarters – in their dressing room they are singing, bawling out, generally celebrating as if they are already world champions. Earlier, watching the Italians walk down the players' tunnel from their bus, Stein has had the unmistakable feeling that they believe they are invincible – he can see it in their eyes.

'Their attitude to us was, "How many goals do you want to lose by today, boys?"' Willie Miller later confirms of the feeling transmitted when lining up in the players' tunnel alongside the Italians. 'You could see that they thought, "Good, here come the Scots, we'll send them packing." They were arrogant.'

As so often before, Stein selects the right team; guessing, correctly, that Italy had employed a physical style against the South American teams because they expected a feast of feuding in those contests and were determined to get their retaliation in first. The Italians, Stein expects, will believe they can defeat the Scots through superior technical ability and this is why they are so exuberant pre-match – they feel as though the pressure, to a degree, is off them after their mammoth contests with the South Americans, whom they respect as equals in playing their type of football.

With one minute gone, Graeme Souness sends a long ball into the Italian penalty area that bounces behind the opposition's defence and sits up just a bit too high for Joe Jordan. He still gets his toe to the ball before Dino Zoff, the Italy goalkeeper, can reach it but the striker's toe-prod flies past the post. Three minutes later Gordon Strachan veers in from the right and clips the ball past Zoff only for it to rebound from the post, too quickly for the Scot who is unable to get the ball out of his feet before Giuseppe Bergomi, the eighteen-year-old Italian defender, slides in to swipe it away from him.

After that fiery start, it becomes a cagey game. Enzo Bearzot, the pipe-smoking Italy manager, white-suited like an ice cream salesman but with arms out of the jacket that he wears across his shoulders stylishly like a lightweight cloak, strides to the touchline and castigates his defenders, berating them civilly from within his sparrow-like frame. The Italians, perhaps atoning for their overconfidence, retreat into caution, playing the ball about carefully at the back, with plenty of passes to Zoff, who dallies on the ball before releasing it every time it is returned to him and who holds up a hand in apology to Juan Cardellino, the Uruguayan referee, when urged to release the ball more quickly. The match becomes soporific, the crowd becomes becalmed and then distracted as people seek means to cope with the heat that attacks them mercilessly and relentlessly inside a stadium with little cover. As the match progresses, more and more spectators make their way to refreshment stalls to stock up with drinks and ice creams, the need for such dominating the mind in a way that would not happen if the encounter on the field of play was more gripping. Even the Scottish supporters, vociferous at the start of the match and outnumbering the Italians, are unable to make much noise at a match that seems to be going nowhere.

The Italians have still not had a shot on goal when Ciccio Graziani, their striker, finds a chink of light in the Scottish defence but, unwilling to snatch at a shot at the expense of losing possession, he turns delicately and, shielding the ball, plays it back to Alessandro Altobelli, the midfield player, who returns it to Graziani only for him to be harried immediately by Miller, and then Wark, who picks him up as he retreats into midfield. Graziani, chased back to his own halfway line, responds with a pass all the way back to Zoff that at least rouses the sleepy crowd to make known their dissatisfaction at seeing an attacker play so stultifyingly dully. Zoff holds on to the ball and makes as if to kick it long but instead drops it to his feet and strolls across his penalty area with it, like a man out for a walk with a dog and patiently waiting for it to do its business. He reaches the edge of the box then turns and strolls back in the direction from which he has just come, before picking up the ball as Jordan comes surging toward him.

Zoff rolls the ball to Gaetano Scirea, the sweeper, who nudges it to Gabriele Oriali. Then it goes to Marco Tardelli, then Fulvio Collovati and back to Scirea who elects to ease it back to Zoff again. None of the Italians has shown any sign of wishing to do more with the ball than take it for a gentle stroll. Zoff, this time, frowns hard at the ball as if it is something he has just seen for the first time in his life; bouncing it four times, as if to assess its weight and flexibility, before dropping it again and taking it for another lazy constitutional.

The clock on the stadium's large electronic scoreboard shows that half of the first half has crept along as Zoff uses his instep to roll the ball, with the urgency of a grandfather playing in the back garden with his two-year-old grandson, to Antonio Cabrini, in the left-back position, who strolls forward unhurriedly as if on an evening promenade, and taps the ball to Bruno Conti, the winger. He turns to face Strachan and plays the ball inside to Tardelli, who bucks the trend by hitting a snappy return for which Conti has to show some pace to click on to the ball again and, having gathered some acceleration, he goes bending outside David Narey and is no sooner past the Scottish defender than he is whisking in a cross that flies across the face of goal, behind the centre-backs. Paolo Rossi, the Italy striker, is in there but appears not to get a touch – except that he clearly has because in one instant the ball is in his vicinity and in the next it has flown behind Rough. It is stinging for the Scots but Italy are 1–0 ahead.

With Scotland utterly shocked at the suddenness of this ghostly goal and its transformative effect on the match, and with the Italians happy to sit on their lead, the game trundles to half-time with little further incident. Steam rises in clouds from the Scottish players, swathed in cold, wet towels, at half-time and Stein bides his time before telling them that he wants them to push forward after the interval. He goes around every player in the team, telling them to advance slightly in their position and to put pressure on the Italians when they have possession, especially when they are playing it around at the back.

Ten minutes into the second half, Souness is sent tumbling by Oriali twenty-five yards from goal. Robertson takes the free-kick, which goes up and over the wall then dips and bends with the elegance of a trained gymnast on the parallel bars before flat-lining toward Zoff's goal. The Italian captain and custodian has been left flat-footed by the pace and precision of Robertson's delivery and is a mere spectator as the ball streaks to his right and . . . clips the outside of the post.

Again the Italians respond cautiously to this warning from the Scots and the game meanders mundanely thanks to Italy's blatant time-wasting methods. Frustration builds and a hefty challenge from Alex McLeish on Conti sends the winger tumbling over an advertising hoarding and into the ranks of the photographers. The Italians rush, en masse, to the site of the offence, their arms raised, their supplicating eyes looking to the sky. A couple of them make for the shoulder of the referee, jostling him, demanding action. He simply waves Zoff to take the goal-kick and the captain, looking as disconsolate as a man who has been told he has lost his life savings, stretches out both arms horizontally in the direction of Conti, still receiving treatment from the doctor, as if to ask how he can go about his work when one of his friends is suffering so much. In fury, simulated or otherwise, he deliberately belts the ball over the left touchline for a throw to the Scots and as Strachan goes to take it, Conti rises to his feet, gingerly, and treads slowly along the perimeter of the pitch, as if taking his first few steps into the water for a paddle at the edge of a chilly ocean. The referee waves him back on to the field and he trudges slowly into position.

When Zoff next receives the ball, a minute or so later, he swiftly, almost as though he is making a point to the referee, throws it out to Conti on the left wing. He quickly prods it away, like a diner distastefully pushing away the remains of a disappointing meal. The impression given is that it is too early for the winger to contemplate anything other than the delicate business of putting one foot in front of the other. Altobelli, a most graceful player, picks it up and turns to go inside, to his right, away from Conti. This draws Narey infield but Altobelli quickly hooks his right boot around the ball to whip a pass out to the left where Conti, suddenly a blur of legs and arms, sets off at a fair old clip into the space vacated by his temporarily distracted opponent.

One touch gets the ball under Conti's control, a second pushes it well ahead of him, into an unguarded stretch of space, giving him time to look up and assess what is going on inside the penalty area. With the third touch of his left boot, he gets under the ball for a cross that curls wide of Rough at the near post, over the head of McLeish in the centre and drops earthward to the back post where Rossi, half-crouching, like a country gent sitting on a shooting stick, meets it with his head and sends the ball swooping over the line. There are twenty minutes remaining but everyone knows there will be no way back for the Scots after this.

Before the match, Stein had looked around the dressing room and felt proud of a team of men who, once they'd put their Scottish shirts on, looked bigger, somehow, than they really are; the jeunesse dorée of the game. After the match, they look like a team of ragged primary school kids. Tears are flowing and every player sits motionless, raging, lost for words, for half an hour, beside themselves. No one speaks. There is nothing to be said. Scotland have lost their grip on the World Cup.

FEELING THE HEAT

There are 160 armed Mexican police escorting Scotland to and from their hotel to training and to the stadiums for their matches at the 1986 World Cup. Those among the players who initially wondered whether this was a bit excessive soon understand why the authorities are just a little bit jumpy about the security of the Scots. Two of their three group-stage matches have been scheduled for a place where desperation rules: Nezahualcóyotl, a sprawling, overcrowded locality on the outskirts of Mexico City. It is one of the largest slums in Latin America: the majority of houses do not have clean running water, sewage systems or electricity; the corpses of dogs, unloved during life, unmourned in death, lie decaying at the side of the road, victims of cars speeding through desperately at full tilt. The Mexican government has cosmetically 'cleaned up' certain other parts of teeming Mexico City in time for the World Cup, but Nezahualcóyotl has too many blemishes for them even to begin such a process and the powers that be have hardly made any effort in that direction. The earthquake that hit the capital only nine months ago brought around one in four of Nezahualcóyotl's shaky buildings quickly crashing to earth and their rubble remains piled high.

Sharp-faced locals stand and watch as the coach carrying the Scotland team whizzes past en route to the stadium for a training session this early June morning, with police outriders, sirens wailing, ensuring its rapid progress. These street-corner observers cannot afford the price of a match ticket to see a World Cup tie even when it is on their doorstep – not when so many of them have to scavenge a living on a massive rubbish dump half a mile from the stadium.

Even the tightest ring of security can occasionally be broken, though, and as Davie Cooper, the Scots' outside-left, is strolling toward the less-than-imposing entrance of the Neza 86 stadium, ready for a loose workout, his way is suddenly blocked. Staring up at him, a powerful, one hundred-watt smile lighting up her face, is a skinny little girl, no more than four years of age, with beautiful, rich, velvety brown eyes; a picture of prettiness in her faded red dress and with a small metal crucifix around her neck. Hands cupped in front of her she meets his gaze, her eyes fixed imploringly, hoping for some money from this rich football player from a different world. A senior policeman, irritated that his men have perhaps become complacent through the Scots' visit having been incident free, yells at two men to remove the intruder but Cooper places a hand on her bony shoulder and signals for them to wait. Bending down, the footballer's face creases into a smile.

'Buenas dias,' he says and she, grinning, replies with a sing-song version of the same greeting.

Kitted out in his training gear, Cooper has no money on him but Hugh Allan, the physiotherapist, hands him a bundle of pesos and Cooper places them in the girl's hands. She scurries off and, just before squeezing through the police cordon, turns and smiles at him again, before melting back into the teeming slum streets. 'Good luck; good luck in your life,' Cooper says gently, in the direction in which she has gone. This is one opponent who has left a greater impression on the winger than most of the rugged defenders who have confronted him in his career.

· 1986 · 1986 · 1986 · 1986 · 1986 · 1986 · 1986 · 1986 · 1986 · 1986 ·

The previous day, Cooper, sitting with Hugh Allan after breakfast, had turned to the physio and told him that what he wished for more than anything was to be at home and taking his dog for a walk on a rainy, Scottish morning. This is no whimsical sentiment. Cooper appreciates the surroundings of the hotel Villa Arqueólogica in Teotihuácan, situated in the vicinity of the pyramids, but after sixteen days of altitude training in Santa Fe, in the US, followed by almost a fortnight in Mexico, Cooper has played only fifteen minutes of competitive football. It has been a long trek for such a short spell of action. The effects of high altitude dictate that it is only possible to train for a couple of hours each day and, though entertainment has been laid on at the hotel by the team management, nothing can remove the sense of confinement and monotony that this degree of inactivity induces. Now, though, with the third of Scotland's group games fast approaching, cooped-up Cooper has a glimmer of renewed hope. During his fifteen minutes on the turf against the West Germans, in the Scots' second match of the tournament, he did well and, though the team lost, his trickery almost produced an equalizer. Cooper has heard whispers that he may have done enough, finally, to be included in the team from the start of the forthcoming match against Uruguay – the Scots' third game.

This is an ill-conceived World Cup. With twenty-four participants parcelled off into six groups, FIFA has devised a freakish method of obtaining the requisite sixteen teams for the start of the knockout stage. Accompanying the winner and runner-up in each group will be the four third-placed teams with the best records and this awkward system means that Scotland, despite having lost to Denmark and the Germans, can qualify for the next round if they extract a victory from their match with Uruguay.

The hosting of the tournament by Mexico is in itself ill conceived; the world's footballers are again being exposed to playing matches at the hottest time of day, despite FIFA's technical committee recommending after the 1970 tournament in the same country that this should never happen again.

None of this matters to Cooper, who is desperate to get his first full taste of the World Cup; he even believes that his style of play is favoured by the conditions here. A hugely skilled left-winger, he relies on beating opponents through mesmeric, close-quarters deception rather than sheer speed; and the conditions in Mexico, where players are slowed down by the altitude, heat and humidity and have to play in short bursts before recovering, favour him. That is how he plays even in the wind and the rain back home. He felt a little bit of tightness across his chest early in the altitude training but nothing after that and, following day after day of training without a match, the anticipation of finally getting ninety minutes has reinvigorated him, bringing back that familiar sense of anticipation that he feels prior to the first match of the league season.

He feels a different person now, rejuvenated, refreshed, and at this, the final training session at the Neza Stadium prior to the following day's match, Cooper is paying special attention to getting a feel for the conditions, concentrating on his shooting in and around the penalty area. He assesses that the combination of the light World Cup ball and playing at altitude makes the ball travel considerably faster inside the box and that it is, therefore, best to stroke it rather than to hit it full on; again this favours the player with a highly developed touch. 'Step forward Mr Cooper,' he says to himself, smiling, as he dispatches another beautifully curved left-footed shot into the top corner of the rigging.

A quiet, undemonstrative man, one who expresses himself almost entirely through his on-field creativity, Cooper digs deep inside himself to obtain pre-match confidence. Now in a highly positive frame of mind, he stops to refresh himself with a cool draught of water and imagines the applause ringing around the stadium from one of his crowd-pleasing moments.

· 1986 · 1986 · 1986 · 1986 · 1986 · 1986 · 1986 · 1986 · 1986 · 1986 ·

The dressing room is like a Turkish bath before the match with the Uruguayans. Cooper, though, is feeling fresh and cool, quietly readying himself, playing over and over again in his mind how he is going to swoop and swerve past defenders and how best to work the pitch with his swift and sudden changes of direction. He is so enveloped in his thoughts that it takes him time to realize that Alex Ferguson, the Scotland caretaker manager, is reading out the team lines and when he reaches the eleventh name on his list and Cooper has not heard his own moniker, it is clear to the player that, with the Uruguayans expected to put the boot in ruthlessly, the manager has decided to go with a starting eleven that will, he feels, best be able to counter the South Americans' approach. That, Cooper knows, right away, means more functional, tougher individuals have been favoured to start the game. It is like a blow to the solar plexus but he decides quickly that he will still ready himself to play and remain in a positive frame of mind. This, after all, could be the final ninety minutes of World Cup action in which he is involved. He cannot afford to become so enervated that any chance he gets to participate is spoiled.

Alex Ferguson's team talk is less than inspirational. He stresses to the players that if they play to their full potential they are the equals of anyone in the competition. There is not enough about how to deal with the Uruguayans – or about the importance of being patient and maintaining possession. Instead it is more the type of team talk that would befit a small team taking on a bigger one in a domestic cup competition.

The Uruguayans seem determined to show, right from the start, that their thuggish reputation is not a false one. After fifty-five seconds José Batista veers out to the wing like a man sent crazy by the heat and cuts through Gordon Strachan with a 'challenge' that cuts the Scot off at the knees. Batista is shown the fastest red card in World Cup history by Joel Quiniou, the French referee, but even with Uruguay down to ten men, the Scots struggle. The players selected may be tough and resilient in the face of the clumsy and heavy challenges they face in British club football but they have never encountered the way the Uruguayans have made gamesmanship a game in itself.

Uruguay players nip and pinch the Scots when the ball is in another part of the pitch; they punch and elbow when the ball is well away; they tread on the fingers of any opponent temporarily grounded; they pull hair; they tug surreptitiously at their opponents' private parts and they spit on the Scots, copiously. All of these tactics are designed to force less sneaky opponents into highly visible retaliation and though the Scottish players have been well warned not to lose their discipline and retaliate, the effect is still a wearing one upon them, continually hampering their naturally robust game. Any tackling by the Scots is met by Uruguayans rolling around and around, disrupting the flow of a game that only splutters and stutters occasionally, as if by accident, into a semblance of football as we know it.

It is Stevie Nicol, a stolid, solid player, who has been preferred to Cooper on the left side of midfield and in one of the rare intervals of fluid football during the first half, Roy Aitken and Gordon Strachan work the ball cleverly together down the right and catch out the Uruguayan defence, all of whom stand frozen as the ball rolls across the penalty area and lands at the feet of Nicol, six yards out and unattended. The South American side are susceptible to balls played in behind their defence across the six-yard box and it is vital that when the Scots prod at this quivering weakness successfully, they make it count. It should be a goal but Nicol seems to hesitate for ever and his balance is all wrong as he goes to strike the ball. His attempt is soft, weak, and the goalkeeper easily scoops up the ball. The chance is gone. Cooper winces on the touchline. It is the best opening of the first half.

The Scottish players, drenched in sweat, covered in cuts and bruises, look a pretty demoralised bunch when they troop in at half-time. They are being jostled out of the game by the Uruguayans and they lack the resources to combat an approach to the game that is alien to them. The Scots' natural aggression is defused by the heat and by the knowledge that the referee, having sent off a Uruguayan, will, like referees the world over, be likely to even that up, if given a clear opportunity.

The pattern of the match continues after half-time and it remains a stifling spectacle, an unengaging struggle, with Cooper observing it all ruefully while performing stretching exercises behind a goal-line. He glances at the stadium clock every other minute and as time ticks away, he wonders if he will ever get his chance. He thinks back to his contribution to Scotland's qualification for the finals: his key, linking role in Kenny Dalglish's goal that sealed the vital win over Spain; his nerveless penalty to clinch the essential draw with Wales on the tragic night in Cardiff when Jock Stein collapsed and died; his precise free-kick that opened the scoring against the Australians in the play-off match for the finals. He knows he is perceived as a maverick but this maverick has, nevertheless, proved himself a most steely and reliable one at the most demanding of times. Despite that recent and decisive impact on the Scotland team, he remains typecast as a luxury player, something that grates with him. Where would Scotland be without this maverick? he thinks to himself. Not at the Mexico World Cup, that's for sure.

Cooper is finally summoned into action, replacing Nicol, with around twenty minutes remaining and is quickly brought into play when Willie Miller eases forward and strokes a ball out to the left wing. When Cooper next opens his eyes he is stretched out on the turf in front of the Scotland team bench, two anxious physiotherapists attending to him. 'What happened?' he asks Eric Ferguson, as the physio peers at him anxiously. 'Well, you went for the ball and next thing one of those Uruguayans had wrapped his boot, studs first, around your throat. So he's off – but how are you?' Groggily, Cooper gets to his feet and provides assurances that he is feeling fit enough to continue despite the bruising around his neck. After some minutes he treads to the touchline to await the referee's attention but while standing there, some of those on the Uruguayan bench hurl sharp-cornered water bags at him, intended as refreshment for parched players but now deployed as part of an anti-Scottish armoury. One bag is thrown with such force and accuracy that it pierces the player's thigh and blood swiftly spurts from the three-inch cut it has made. A barney breaks out between the two team benches and Cooper is forced to delay his re-entry to the action as he receives some paper stitches back in the dressing room, where a patch of plaster is applied to cover up the site of the wound.

Twelve minutes have now passed since Cooper first attempted to take to the pitch and when the battered, wounded player finally gets back on, he is, as had been intended by his opponents, feeling a good deal less fresh than a substitute ought to be. There are six minutes remaining when he finally gets his first touch of the ball. Paul McStay finds him with a short pass and Cooper, having cut inside to a central area, has space to work with as he slips past one defender, then a second, the ball bobbling on his left foot, like a playful kitten. When Fernando Álvez, the goalkeeper, advances to confront him on the edge of his six-yard box, Cooper, for good measure, slips around him too. His momentum having taken him almost to the goal-line, he clips a low ball, caressed with his instep, into the Uruguay goal; Eduardo Acevedo, the Uruguay captain, can only help it into the net. It is enough to prod Scotland into the last sixteen and a match with Argentina. You can always trust a maverick.

There was still enough scope, in the remaining minutes of the Uruguay match, for one of the opposition to present Cooper with a small souvenir of the encounter: a defender stamped on his foot, and did so with such practice and accuracy that the stud penetrated the flap of the boot and left a small hole in the top of the Scot's foot. When he turns up for treatment on it the following morning, he finds the designated room crammed with every participant from the previous day's match; all requiring varying degrees of attention after their battle with the Uruguayans.

· 1986 · 1986 · 1986 · 1986 · 1986 · 1986 · 1986 · 1986 · 1986 · 1986 ·

This is a strange World Cup for the Scots. Expectations of them have been low ever since Kenny Dalglish withdrew from the squad a few days prior to departure for Mexico. The SFA had even booked the players' flights back to Glasgow on the day after completion of the opening, group stage; a precaution made against the possibility of the team winging its way home after the first round but something that became a disastrous faux pas for the SFA when the story was leaked to the press. It then emerged that some players had booked to take their summer holidays at the same time as the second phase of the World Cup, seeming evidence that some of the participants may share the administrators' pessimism about the team's chances of success in the heat and dust of Central America.

'Hey, Paul,' Cooper says, tapping Paul McStay's shoulder with a magazine as he enters the treatment room. 'Sorry to put the kybosh on starting our holidays early and all that.'

McStay smiles, a Clyde Valley tomato in one hand; he has brought with him a seemingly unending personal supply of this delicacy from his homeland.

'Is it the kybosh or have you just delayed us making a splash at Magaluf only for a wee day or two?' Frank McAvennie interjects.

'What do you mean?' Cooper asks, sharply.

'Well, have you not seen that we're playing Argentina in the next game? Nobody told you? Argentina . . . And Argentina means Maradona. Diego Armando Maradona . . .' McAvennie stretches out the full name, lingering on every syllable in the manner of the local commentators when lost in the excitement of another piece of Maradona magic at this tournament.

'Okay, okay,' Cooper says. 'So he's got a middle name – but he's only got one mother, like the rest of us.'

'Aye,' Willie Miller says, looking up from his copy of the *Financial Times*, flown in freshly from the UK, 'so he has; just the one mother. The only problem is she's Wonderwoman.'

'He's only human,' Alex McLeish chimes in, 'just like Mozart only had one pair of hands when he was composing all those symphonies – and "Elvira Madigan" is just a wee tune.'

'I'm just saying,' Cooper continues, 'that we must have a chance. Maradona is good, but he can have an off day, or we can stop him. If we go out thinking he's going to run riot, we've got no chance at all. Tell me this, who else can you name in the Argentina team? Nobody. So are we going to accept that a one-man team is going to get the better of us?'

Silence; the other players seem to be contemplating his remarks. The lack of chat quickly draws their attention to Graeme Souness, lightly snoring in the corner. 'Hey, listen to this,' Willie Miller says, producing a Scottish tabloid that has arrived along with his financial bible. He reads stentoriously:

> He could play in any league in the world –
> Italy or Spain – and England would be a breeze
> for him. He is as talented as anyone I've ever
> seen; explosive as dynamite. He's what you would
> call an honest conman; full of legitimate trickery
> but still likely to make opponents feel as though
> they have been swindled.

'Right,' Miller says, 'Your starter for ten: who is talking and who is he talking about? And it's not Maradona.'

There are no takers. 'Hey Souey,' Miller shouts, stirring Souness into action, the latter's moustache quivering as he is awoken from his nap. 'What's all this "Explosive as dynamite"?' Miller turns to Cooper, 'It's you, Coop, this is Souness talking about you.'

Souness laughs, turns over and goes back to sleep; Jimmy Steele, the masseur moving over to give him a rub-down, even though Souness has missed the match with Uruguay, having been dropped, audaciously, by Ferguson. Now thirty-three years old, the powerfully built Souness has struggled perhaps more than anyone else with the strength-sapping heat in Mexico.

Cooper had, before the tournament, heard all about Ferguson – the strict disciplinarian who had performed miracles at Aberdeen through keeping a tight rein on his players.

241

Out here in Mexico, though, and earlier in Santa Fe, Ferguson has been surprisingly relaxed and friendly; a man with rules, sure, but charming and helpful when coaxing the best out of his players. This World Cup feels a bit less taut, a bit less tense than usual for the Scots.

Around Cooper, the players settle down again. Richard Gough is reading *The Little Drummer Girl*, John le Carré's latest novel, while Jim Leighton is intent on a game of computer chess. This evening the players and management will again mingle in the piano bar: Alex Ferguson will be fun and Steelie will do his song-and-dance-man thing. Maybe, just maybe, Cooper feels, this is the way to do it over here in Mexico; keep everyone in a happy frame of mind, maintain low expectations, and then maybe just smooth our way to the final with the players as surprised as anyone at the outcome.

· 1986 · 1986 · 1986 · 1986 · 1986 · 1986 · 1986 · 1986 · 1986 · 1986 ·

Cooper is convinced that Scotland can live with Maradona and his conviction becomes firmer when he is named in the team for the match, in Puebla at the Cuauhtémoc Stadium, another modest venue that appears almost custom-built to cut the Argentinians down to size. Cooper's conviction that he can contribute to the downfall of Maradona becomes even stronger when Ferguson stresses to him that Argentina will be using a 3–5–2 system, one new to the game and which should leave plenty of space for him on the wing and in behind the Argentinians' defence if he is sharp and quick enough to react when the ball comes his way. The injuries he sustained in the Uruguay match have healed and Cooper feels good, perfectly primed to give of his best and sure that he and his team-mates can perform with excellence.

Cooper, like many footballers, is not a great watcher of the game. The last time he stood on the terraces was in 1965 when Scotland faced Italy in a World Cup qualifying match. Nor does he trust television's coverage of the game too much, feeling it offers a restricted view of the full flow of a match. Both the media and the punters have been puffing up Maradona's talents for a long time but Cooper, as with many serious professionals, distrusts their views and opinions as being essentially those of amateurs. So it is only when finally on the pitch at the Cuauhtémoc Stadium that Cooper can gauge precisely how good Maradona is. His confidence in himself and his team is such that his first reaction to watching Maradona on the ball is to say to himself, 'He's all left foot, just like me.' Then, as Maradona grabs the game and keeps grasp of it, tightly, Cooper realizes he is seeing someone and something unique.

This five-foot-five-inch muscular man, with thighs as thick as a bull's, weaves in and out of close challenges the way a racing driver might squeeze around a series of bollards. Maradona's fifth-minute goal is a portrait in persistence and perfection. He bursts from midfield, ball spinning on his toe, and as Miller closes in, Maradona swerves slightly to his right then instantaneously accelerates, immediately transforming the defender from challenger to pursuer. David Narey converges on the duo, both running, but Maradona puts on another spurt of speed and now bends his run to swerve away from Narey, as Alex McLeish joins in pursuit. Maradona, towered over by the Scots, keeps possession immaculately, fending off nudges and dunts for thirty yards before sending the ball to Jorge Valdano on his right.

The Scottish defenders, finally relieved of their pursuit of the Argentinian number ten, relax for a second but that is a second too long as Valdano quickly returns the ball to Maradona, who, briefly unattended, sprints on to it inside the penalty area and, as Jim Leighton advances, applies an exquisite touch to the ball that takes it past the outrushing goalkeeper. Leighton's presence seems to have ensured that the ball, even though it's going past him, will also go wide; but Maradona has left so much spin on the ball that its first bounce directs it, as if by remote control, unerringly into the Scottish net. It is a goal scored with an awe-inspiring display of practised precision and improvisation.

It is a fitting overture for a match in which Maradona, moving with the grace of a dancer, conducts every sweeping move made by his team in the Scottish half of the field. When, during the second half, another fine Maradona goal is disallowed by Luigi Agnolin, the Italian referee, Cooper, awestruck, momentarily feels disappointment at the decision before remembering this is an opponent and that a place in the last eight is at stake. Maradona has that effect; appreciation of his talents dissolves barriers. The Scots, at the match's conclusion, have managed to keep the score down to 1–0 but long before the end it is clear that this is Argentina's match – in Maradona's World Cup.

HELPING HANDS

No senior FIFA official would ever become involved in accepting a bribe in connection with the great game of football. That is a given. Nor would a senior Austrian Football Association official ever become involved in offering a bribe. It is unthinkable. It just would not happen. Not even when a place in the last sixteen of the World Cup is at stake and not even when that place is to be allocated on the strength of a drawing of lots. No, if any dirty work were ever to be contemplated, no experienced football official would ever wish to have anything to do with it.

This is why Rudolf Mock, a twenty-one-year-old junior official with the Austrian FA at the 1990 World Cup, receives an anonymous telephone call in his three-star hotel in Florence,

Italy, shortly after breakfast on the morning of 22 June 1990, a day that will conclude with FIFA drawing lots at a special ceremony in Rome to decide whether Austria or Scotland, two nations with identical records in the group stage of the tournament, should proceed into the knockout stages. 'Now listen carefully, follow instructions and don't interrupt,' the voice from the other end of the telephone intones in the clipped, Austrian regional dialect that Mock recognizes as being from his own Linz region. 'You must do your national duty. In your hotel mailbox, downstairs, you will find the key for a left-luggage locker at the central station in Zürich. You will travel from Florence to Zürich today, on the noon train. At the station in Zürich, you will open the locker and remove from it a sports bag. The bag contains a small cardboard box with a substantial sum of money inside it. You will immediately and discreetly remove the bag and repair to the James Joyce Pub on the Pelikanstrasse and at six o'clock you will take a seat on the terrace, where you will order an Irish coffee.

'A man will approach you – he will know you by the drink on the table in front of you. He does not know who you are or what you are going to say. You will remain at the table but only for a minute or two and then you will leave; also leaving the sports bag on your side of the table. You will depart from the pub slowly and unobtrusively and you will then make your way back to Vienna. You will not return to the team hotel in Italy and you will stay away from the headquarters of the Football Association until after the conclusion of the World Cup tournament. I will not be in touch with you again but I expect and know that you will carry out these instructions meticulously and, if you do, be assured that a bright future awaits you.'

The chance to work in Vienna has been a dream opportunity for Mock. A keen amateur footballer but never good enough to make the grade, he opted to leave school for a trainee managerial post in a Linz department store and the accompanying steady salary rather than take the place at university that was on offer to him. Tedium had quickly enveloped him in the job so when the chance arose to combine his usefulness with figures and a post in administration at the Austrian FA in Vienna, he quickly took it – and to be present at the World Cup in Italy has been a gold-spun stroke of good fortune. It beats dealing with *hausfraus* spoiling for a fight over returned goods and accounting for every *pfennig* at the end of a working day.

Now, though, entrusted with being a key component in what is clearly an important operation – something made clear by the secrecy surrounding it – he is all nerves and not the smooth, unruffled senior-administrator-to-be that he pictures in his mind's eye. He has watched, in Florence, the way in which major figures inside the Austrian FA operate with practised assuredness: the expensively cut suits, the cigars, the easy handshakes, the small-talk at cocktail parties, the chauffeur-driven cars. He wants a part of it and is terrified of blowing his big opportunity to prove himself and move closer to this inner circle of influence and prosperity.

Safely transported north over the Swiss border into Zürich, and now sitting in the terrace of the James Joyce Pub, Mock tries to look settled and assured but his heart is pounding hard enough, he feels, for it to burst out of his chest, and he senses the blood coursing around his veins like a fast-rushing river. He places the Irish coffee, together with a bar of Toblerone that he has been eating, on the table in front of him and waits. He had at one stage been concerned that the telephone call could have been a ruse, a trick, a practical joke, even though the Austrian FA is not noted for being a fun-filled institution, but having conferred quietly with Hans Schneinze, his mentor inside the FA, he has received immediate assurances that this is an urgent mission and one to be undertaken not lightly but with professionalism and speed.

At precisely six o'clock, a thin man, he could even be a tin man for his lack of animation, sits down at a ninety-degree angle to Mock and stares straight ahead. A narrow black tie and jet-black hair are what Mock will remember most significantly about his contact and, nerves jangling, thoughts scrambled, he cannot remember what exactly he ought to do or not to do before leaving behind the bag. He stares at the Toblerone and, for want of anything else to say or do, in friendly fashion offers his table-sharer a piece, 'Sch-sch-schokolade?' The man starts slightly on hearing the rushed-out word, spoken in a jittery, guttural Linz accent, then returns to staring straight ahead. Seemingly ignored by his contact, and with his chocolate ignored too, Mock hurriedly gathers up the confectionery and, keen to leave without further ado, exits the pub having left the bag at his table.

Half an hour later, a telephone rings in Rome's Excelsior hotel. The call is from Zürich and the speaker is an independent Swiss-based operative acting as a go-between for two parties with whom he wishes to establish no connection. The message he relays is, 'All is in order. Business may proceed.

The word I have is . . . "Sch-schokolade".' He pronounces the word – he is trained to pass on without comment anything he is told by a contact in the event that it is code – down the crackly Italian telephone line, precisely as he has heard it. There is a slight pause on the other end of the line before it goes dead. The recipient of the call proceeds immediately to the dining room of the hotel, where he finds a young girl, sitting alone at table number sixteen, flicking through a maga-zine. 'Everything is in order to go forward – and the word is . . . "Schott-o-land",' he tells her as he pulls up a chair at her table. The girl smiles and says, loud enough for the other tables in the vicinity to hear, 'Yes, I'll have a coffee, thank you. I'll just go and freshen up.'

Whooshed by the lift to the fifth floor, she knocks on a room door that is opened just wide enough for the person inside to cram his head into the tiny space between the door and its frame. She can hear a rich murmur of conversation from farther inside the room as she says, 'All is okay. Word is "Schottland".' The door is snapped shut so swiftly that she has to jump to avoid being struck by it. Inside, the man who now knows 'the word' bustles diagonally across the expen-sively furnished room where half a dozen well-tailored men, comfortably late-middle-aged or early elderly, are chatting away complacently, over drinks and smokes, with the smell of expensive cologne enfolding the room. The latest recipient of the message leans down toward one of the men and repeats what he has been told in his ear, eliciting from the seated man a mild, almost indistinguishable mew of surprise at the word proffered to him. The name of Scotland is not normally asso-ciated with anything underhand, he thinks. Now had it been the other way around . . . Business is business, though, so he puts down his not-quite-finished brandy, rises to his feet, draws his hand over his thinning, pomaded hair, buttons his jacket and says, 'Well gentlemen, I hear that everything is now in place for the drawing of lots for the next stage of the fourteenth World Cup. The world's media awaits us. Shall we proceed downstairs and complete the formalities?'

And that is how Scotland came to proceed into the last sixteen of Italia '90 at the expense of the grand old footballing nation of Austria.

· 1990 · 1990 · 1990 · 1990 · 1990 · 1990 · 1990 · 1990 · 1990 · 1990 ·

'You know,' Jack Charlton, the Ireland manager, intones on the television commentary as the Romania–Scotland last-sixteen tie enters its closing stages, 'if we had remained in the competition, I would not have minded one little bit, not one little bit, if we had gone all the way to the final without winning a game. Penalties are part of the game and it will now come down to which side has the best goalkeeper.' The man from the North-East of England pronounces the final word in his sentence idiosyncratically as 'ghoul-keeper' and though his comments will haunt those who enjoy the finer things in football, his logic suits a tournament in which cautious, unattractive tactics prevail and which will see the highest number of games settled by penalty shootout of any World Cup finals.

There are only two minutes remaining of this particular dour and dogged contest and, with neither side having scored, the Scots look duly set for their own first ever World Cup penalty shootout. Romania and Scotland have reversed their way through this game, playing the ball backwards more often than forward.

In another cagey innovation that helps to strangle further open, expansive football, managers at this World Cup have favoured the new 'tactic' of introducing substitutes in the final minute of a match – nothing more than another time-wasting device. This could easily be eliminated by preventing substitutions in, say, the final ten minutes but FIFA sail blithely on, regardless; the corporate hotel suites enjoyed by its officials are just as comfortable at the end of each day, regardless of the quality of the football. Now, with one minute remaining of this desperate slog, anyone hoping for a final flurry of action has their hopes dashed as the Romanians signal that they wish to introduce a replacement and the action seizes up as Daniel Timofte is brought into the fray. This substitution is not solely for the purpose of frittering away time but because Timofte is a penalty-taking expert.

Penalties have an almost magnetic appeal for the more mediocre football managers. A defeat in open play can be blamed upon some perceived failing in the manager or his team – and can be analyzed over and over again on television, in slow-motion, until the cosseted studio experts have nailed the culprits once and for all. Losing a match on penalties, however, is always attributed to chance, bad luck, the vagaries of the gods. Anyone can miss a penalty is the cliché that prevails. It leaves manager and team with reputation intact and the losers even retain a degree of sympathy for their misfortune in having their fate decided in such a fashion.

As the clock ticks down towards penalties, players' thoughts inevitably drift towards the shootout. There is less urgency about the play, with both sides more unwilling than ever to face the ignominy of giving away an unfortunate goal when the delicious prospect of the status-salvaging lottery is around the corner.

José Ramiz Wright, the Brazilian referee, has already looked at his watch three times and has checked time remaining with his linesmen when Florin Raducioiu, the Romania forward, lazily decides to concede a free-kick in midfield through an ankle tap on Paul McStay rather than chase his opponent down the Romanians' left. There is a listlessness about both teams as Scotland commit only four men forward, cautiously leaving the rest of the team to linger in the vicinity of the halfway line even though Romania have crammed every man inside their own penalty area. Roy Aitken strolls toward the ball unhurriedly, checking with the referee, unusually pedantically, as to the exact spot from which the kick should be taken, as if that is important. The Scotland captain makes a further fuss over stilling the ball before casually scooping a punt high into the Romanian penalty area. The ball sails to its far side, where it falls to Mircea Rednic to make an easy clearance with his left boot but he mishits it, slicing the ball back into the centre of his own penalty area. Gica Popescu goes to head it clear, only to find the ball just too high for him and it travels through to Ioan Andone, who is caught out by only seeing the ball at the last moment, thanks to it being blocked from him by Popescu's leap, and it bounces off Andone's knee back towards Silviu Lung in the Romania goal. Although Lung has been drawn to his near post, it looks an easy ball for him to collect by moving nimbly to his left – until he slips and is left clawing at thin air as the ball drifts slowly past him to send this solid, stolid, deliberate, hard-working Scotland team into the quarter-finals of the 1990 World Cup.

Antonio Gabardo Mendes da Monta, from Estoril in Portugal, has been dreaming of a day like this one from the moment he took up refereeing. A quarter-final of the World Cup is only a couple of strides away from the peak of any referee's career – officiating at a World Cup final. A good performance in today's quarter-final would go a long way towards FIFA appointing him as referee for the ultimate match. With Portugal not involved in this tournament he can be counted on for his neutrality – whereas, he believes, FIFA may be more wary of appointing the referees from the several major nations contesting the concluding stages of Italia '90. It helps him, he feels, that an encounter between Italy and Scotland should not be too fraught. 'Ahhhhh, it's English fair play,' is exactly what he relaxedly tells his wife when phoning home to Estoril the night before the match, 'against an Italy on their best behaviour in front of guests in their own sitting room.' Scotland–Italy looks far less problematic to him than a meeting of two of the Latin nations or a match such as Holland–West Germany in the previous round, an encounter laden with historical baggage and consequently hard to handle. And Diego Maradona is nowhere in sight.

Da Monta, a keen footballer, was forced to give up the game as a semi-professional player at third division level when suffering cartilage damage in both knees at the age of twenty-two. A recuperation period that stretched over the best part of a season and which included separate operations on each knee deprived him of his place in his team. Then, while gently finding his feet – and his knees – again as he regained fitness, he was asked by the club to fill in as a referee one afternoon when the designated official had failed to make it for a midweek friendly. He performed so well that members of the club suggested he might have found his vocation; a double-edged compliment in which da Monta chose only to see the good. So steady and sure has been his subsequent movement upward through the ranks of officiators that at thirty-eight he is one of the youngest referees in the World Cup in Italy and rated as one of the most progressive in the business.

This reputation is based largely on the impression that da Monta gives on the pitch of being the next best thing to a player; of understanding not just the rules but how the game is played and duly interpreting on-field events in a practical, non-pedantic way that helps the game to flow and that earns him the players' respect. He talks to players as equals, rather than talking down to them. Da Monta even looks like a player. A job in a bank, with regular hours year-round, means he can maintain a demanding fitness programme and, with his slim physique and head of copious, curly, highly styled dark brown hair, he is the twenty-third man on the pitch; the only referee in the tournament you can imagine climbing into a Ferrari alongside a high-maintenance companion after the game.

A quick smile to both captains and da Monta, ball under arm, leads out the teams for the quarter-final at the Olympic Stadium in Rome, with 75,000 supporters, almost entirely Italian, swirling the green, white and red tricolour of the home nation and creating an unearthly din. Here I am, da Monta thinks, the focus of the entire world this glorious Saturday evening, all eyes on me, the man with the ball, as I cross the white line and take to the field. Around the globe, one billion people are expecting great things from me; they know that on my shoulders rests the burden of ensuring that this is a great football match, that the ebb and flow of the game resides with me, that I can make it a classic match or a drab one, a day to remember or a day best forgotten.

Following the national anthems, da Monta parades to the centre circle, head held proudly high. Maurice Johnston, the Scotland striker, asks him if he can have the ball to get a brief 'feel of it', as they say, but da Monta waves him away imperiously before planting the ball on the centre spot and placing his right boot upon it, hands upon hips, looking all around him, drinking in the fiercely nationalistic sights and sounds in this vast, covered bowl, reverberating with emotion. The enjoyment of these people, da Monta thinks again, is in my hands. 'Just think,' he tells himself, 'if it had not been for that unfortunate injury that cut me down in my prime, I could have been a player on a night like this.'

Once the game begins, da Monta's experience ensures the game moves along efficiently and slickly. It is an intriguing contest, with the Italians, who have played in fits and starts throughout the tournament, struggling to find some rhythm in the face of Scottish intransigence. Totò Schillaci, the bug-eyed Sicilian striker, smacks a shot off the underside of the Scottish crossbar midway through the first half and the ball bounces dangerously in the penalty area before Alex McLeish gets it clear. 'Where was the man following up?' da Monta says to himself as he looks on disbelievingly from the edge of the penalty area. 'You should always be following up, ready to pounce in the event of a half-chance. Goodness me, there are few enough chances at this level so you have to be ready to take those that do come your way.'

It is 0–0 at half-time and the second half maintains the pattern of the first: the Scots defending deep and playing on the break; the Italians carefully trying to build but stifled by their own fear of committing too many players forward and leaving themselves vulnerable. It is a match entirely typical of Italia '90. Another rare chance falls to Schillaci when Roberto Donadoni's rising shot is parried by Jim Leighton, the Scotland goalkeeper. Da Monta is almost on Schillaci's shoulder when the rebound falls to him at an angle to goal. Use your right foot, your right! da Monta is screaming internally at the player as he moves on to the ball but the striker uses his left to try to catch the goalkeeper out at his near post, Leighton grasps the ball and the opportunity is gone.

The match weaves onwards and there are two minutes remaining when da Monta awards a corner to the Scots, on the left. Murdo MacLeod takes it short to Paul McStay, to da Monta's frustration. What are you fiddling about for? he thinks, why don't you get the ball over quickly? Why waste a corner like that, playing it short, when people are waiting inside the area? McStay, though, does catch the referee out by quickly sending the ball over but he flights it too long for Stuart McCall, the advanced midfield player, and there are no Scots at the back post as the ball, set nicely at head-height, hurtles in that direction. 'That's just too easy for an Italian defence to clear,' da Monta says to himself as he watches the ball fly in the direction of Paolo Maldini, positioned perfectly, on the far edge of the six-yard box, to gather the ball and move away with it. A player with his impeccable technique won't make any mistake if the ball reaches him, da Monta tells himself, and, before he knows what he is doing, the referee has launched himself gloriously into the air, springing off those two long-mended knees and using his elongated, athletic frame to rise, he meets the ball and sends a perfect, glancing header past Walter Zenga, the Italy goalkeeper, who cannot, on this occasion, be blamed in any way for having been caught unawares. For a few seconds, da Monta awaits the roar of acclaim from the crowd until he realizes with horror what he has just done. This is how, with the Olympic Stadium and all of Italy in utter uproar, Scotland progress into the semi-finals of the 1990 World Cup.

· 1990 · 1990 · 1990 · 1990 · 1990 · 1990 · 1990 · 1990 · 1990 · 1990 ·

This is the first World Cup at which outsize television screens are in place inside the tournament venues and there are two at the San Paolo Stadium in Naples, one at each end of the ground, high above the supporters' heads. Advertisements from FIFA's official World Cup sponsors – the same images, on a continuous loop, at every game – flash up on the screens before kick-off, so that the beery, bleary fans below are shown such apposite delights as clean-cut, smiling, super-fit specimens benefiting from the latest in superior shaving technology; similarly glowing, healthy individuals refreshing themselves moderately – unlike the fans – at beachside cafes with the official beer plus more of the same for the official video cassette manufacturer, the official camera film manufacturer, the official car, the official soft drink and the official chocolate. It is all repeated so often during the tournament that if you had been trapped inside the World Cup these past few weeks you would think these brands had eliminated every last one of their competitors and had created a brave new, sanitized world in which they are now standing side by side in all their glory.

Slick as it all is, technology is still subject to the occasional glitch. Thus, while the players of Argentina and Scotland are warming up on the pitch, getting gradually used to the balmy conditions twenty minutes before kick-off in their World Cup semi-final, a feed from the BBC studio accidentally segues into place on the big screens instead of the ads and a

257

sharp-featured, English pundit with a distinctive, south London accent is soon braying all over the heads of the fans below.

'The thing about Scotland,' this pundit says flatly, 'is that their typical game is very straightforward and easy to analyse – there isn't any football to be played. Heh, heh, heh.' His characteristic chuckle invites the other studio guests to join in but with him not having said anything funny, nobody does.

'The thing is, other countries' managers know how Scotland play,' he continues, 'and it is an almost medieval style they use – but because Scotland are effectively not playing football, there is nothing the managers can do about it and the more they try to cater for what the Scots are doing, the more likely they are to interfere with their own approach and go down to that basic level and that suits the near-Neanderthal – if I might suggest such a thing – way the Scots go about their business. That, then, gives Scotland a real chance of putting their opponents in trouble. I say this with the greatest respect and as someone who does like the Scots . . . But I am sure that even the most patriotic Scot would agree with me that this is not a particularly good Scottish team – I mean . . .'

The image flickers and then fades away to be replaced with vitamin-enriched models with wholly healthy smiles frolicking on a beach and horses crashing through waves as the World Cup's official sponsors regain control of the medium. The Scottish players resume their warm-up, a few irritable glances among them, a few smiles at the daftness of it all. 'Somebody up there doesn't like us,' Craig Levein, the centre-back, suggests to Jim Leighton, the goalkeeper.

After seventeen minutes of a fiercely contested semi, Claudio Caniggia, Argentina's straw-haired striker, springs into the air to flick a header into the Scottish net. A power surge brings the screens, usually silenced during the match, to life and the voice of the BBC's pundit crackles across the ether. 'Well, that was a very poor goal to lose. Shocking defending. Where was the cover? Now, if that had been the England defence there would have been a man assigned to Caniggia at all times. How can you leave a player of his ability completely unmarked?' The image fades again as the Scots kick off, reinvigorated for the fray, fired by the all-seeing pundit's words.

Two minutes after the Argentinian goal, Julio Olarticoechea, the Argentina defender, and Roy Aitken go for the ball out at the corner flag. The Argentinian, sliding in from the side, gets something on it to send it spinning away from Aitken, but as it rolls toward the corner flag it is caught by the stick and rebounds into play where Aitken scoops it up with his right boot and speeds into the penalty area. His initial shot is blocked by Sergio Goycochea, the goalkeeper, but Aitken gathers the rebound and slots it into the far corner of the goal just as three Argentinians hit him fast, low and hard.

A bustling affair now degenerates into a brutal battle, the Argentinians kicking out and lashing out at the Scots at every opportunity. This is a workmanlike Argentina, unlike the 1986 model, and though Diego Maradona remains in the side he is a slowed-down version of his previous self, still with a great eye for a pass but no longer the mobile, darting demon of 1986.

As the Scots trot out for the second half, the BBC feed again interrupts the ads and the pundit, flickering into life again like Big Brother's mad relation, opines, 'The Argentinians should never have lost that goal. It was unlike them to allow a player so limited and one-paced – with all due respect – as Aitken to get through and they should really have made their superiority count by now. I'm sure they will settle into their stride in this half so, I'm afraid, I don't hold out much hope for Scotland now, much as I do like the Scots . . .'

The Argentinians swing into their stride right away, as the pundit suggested they would, Olarticoechea whacking Maurice Johnston, José Serrezuela whacking Stuart McCall, Juan Simon whacking Paul McStay. Ricardo Giusti takes things a step farther and launches a two-footed tackle at Murdo MacLeod that sees the Argentinian sent off. The Scots press up, seeking to make the most of the extra man and from an Aitken corner, Alex McLeish rises above a scrum of bodies to send a back-header spinning towards goal. Seemingly oddly, the Argentinians have placed Diego Maradona, and not a defender, on the back post and the ball bounces awkwardly up at him off the cut-up turf – too high for him to kick, too wide for a nudge of the thigh, too low for a header. It calls for divine intervention to prevent a goal so Maradona calls into action the hand of God once more, flicking the ball away quickly with his wrist. Erik Fredriksson, the Swedish referee, misses it completely and the linesman's view is muddied by the heap of bodies in the goalmouth. The Scots, deflated at being cheated out of a goal, lose concentration briefly, and when Maradona turns swiftly on the ball in the centre circle and sends a sweet pass shooting into the path of Caniggia, the striker is free to stretch out a boot and send the ball coursing wide of Jim Leighton's outstretched right hand and into the corner of the net. Pundits and press will rave about this goal but they overlook its background – and how a deflated Scottish team, concentration disrupted, had been susceptible to such probing.

That, then, is how Scotland are kicked, pushed, pulled, manhandled and cheated out of the benighted, blighted 1990 World Cup.

YOU COULDN'T MAKE IT UP

Everyone should have a Jack Nicholson moment, Hugh Masterton thinks to himself as he stands outside the Stade de France with ninety minutes remaining before kick-off in the opening match of the 1998 World Cup in Paris. He is standing almost motionless in a recess of the exterior stadium wall, awaiting the arrival of two friends, and taking in the busy, swirling throng of supporters, when he spots Nicholson amid them. The celebrated American movie star, a squat figure, and aged sixty-one now, is able to walk along unhindered because most fans are, like him, on the move and keenly seeking their entrance gate, or a souvenir programme-seller, or looking for their friends.

Nicholson, wearing shades, a dark suit and tie over a white

shirt and carrying an attaché case, becomes aware of Masterton's startled stare and turns his head slowly, in segmented, near-robotic instalments, in the Scot's direction; years of stardom having instilled in him an awareness of being observed closely. Nicholson shoots Masterton an unfriendly, slightly menacing glance, that looks to have been well honed down the years to warn off obsessive fans and other crazies and that carries an unmistakable whiff of 'keep your distance, pal, or I'll make sure you fry in hell', or some other similarly pleasant and simmeringly aggressive, pithy piece of advice that you might expect from an American with expertise in making unwanted confrontations short and sharp affairs on and off screen. Masterton can almost hear in his head the actor saying those very words in his characteristic slow drawl and he watches Nicholson all the way as he veers in an arc down towards the welcoming VIP entrance of the Stade.

That alone, Masterton thinks, was almost worth the price of the ticket: just to be here and have Jack shoot him such a menacing look. The actor is now best known and loved for such films as *The Witches of Eastwick* and *Batman* but Masterton believes they are diluted, chasing-the-dollar, measures of his talent – for him the Nicholson of *Chinatown*, *Easy Rider* and *The Passenger* is the genuine article, largely untrammelled by celebrity and all its attendant means of watering down the acting in the actor. Nowadays, Masterton muses, it actually takes Jack all his time to play his last great role – that of Jack Nicholson, the premier elder-statesman-cum-wild-man of Hollywood. The moment of reverie over, the clamour around him arrests Masterton's attention and he tries once again to anticipate what he expects from the afternoon's action on the football field. The thing is that, unlike with cinema and culture in general, he hasn't got a clue.

· 1998 · 1998 · 1998 · 1998 · 1998 · 1998 · 1998 · 1998 · 1998 · 1998 ·

The chance to join the Tartan Army at the World Cup was too good for Masterton to turn down, especially as the tourney is just across the channel this year. Masterton doesn't even have to take any serious holiday from his solicitor's office to be with Scotland in France and that means he can also have his fortnight's holiday, his real break, in July in the Dominican Republic. The Paris match, for example, is part of a one-night trip: just a trifle over £500 for a return flight from Edinburgh that brought him out to the French capital on the morning of today's game and that will whisk him back at dawn tomorrow, in time to be back at his desk for nine sharp, having stayed the night with a colleague who works in the oil industry and who maintains an apartment in Paris. Also, with there being no cricket or rugby World Cup this year, Masterton can give the jolly old footie all his attention.

A football-loving colleague, unusual in Edinburgh's legal world, has regaled Masterton with tales of how, in the 1970s, the size of the Tartan Army at the '74 World Cup grew by the day, as working-class lads, inspired by the team's performances during the tournament, walked out on their jobs to hitchhike or take the train to West Germany and then sleep under hedges so they could be there to give Scotland their support. Masterton has listened with interest and feels imbued with the spirit of those past exploits; all the time still thankful that he can bypass any similar hardship with the flick of a credit card.

It was the firm itself that had enabled him to be in France. A senior partner had been provided with a haul of twenty-five tickets for the opening game, one of thousands of batches for this World Cup that are being channelled through corporate bodies via sponsors rather than going on sale to the more rough-and-ready supporters. The opening game being Brazil against Scotland, Masterton happily bought up some for himself and a couple of his friends and here he is, ready to have his senses immersed in the experience of being part of the famous Tartan Army for the first time. He is a football fan, he tells himself, otherwise he wouldn't be here, would he? No, he doesn't follow any particular team but he was at a Hearts–Hibs New Year game a few years ago and enjoyed the experience: a few drinks in the pub beforehand, the refreshing cold air clearing the grogginess in the head after the annual festivities, a post-match jar of Polish jam purchased from the delicatessen on the corner of the street beside the stadium – only in Edinburgh – and then pie and chips on the way home. Great stuff, he recalls, great atmosphere; though he can't remember very much about the match itself; not even the final score.

Now, in Paris, having met up with his pals, Midge – an ironically named six-foot-seven rugby player – and Tucks – whose school and university nickname has stuck with him because of his continuing, serious enjoyment of grub – Masterton ascends with them their allotted internal staircase at the Stade, tingling with anticipation, and he is not disappointed. A troupe of gymnasts, acrobats, stilt walkers, clowns and mime artists are gambolling, jumping and bouncing around on trampolines and mats that have been laid over the pitch for the tournament's opening ceremony. 'Wow,' Masterton exclaims to his pals, as they emerge into the light and take their seats, 'this gives you a bigger bang for your buck. We're at more than a football match, aren't we?'

Despite having shelled out happily for the highest-priced

ticket available – a cool £110 – Masterton and friends find them- selves planted high in one corner of the stadium, over- looking the corner flag. To their right, the entire central chunk of seats, in prime position for the best view of the game, is filled with a neutral, dun-coloured heap; rows of bodies whose grey and dark suits contrast severely with the blues and yellows of the Scots and Brazilian fans all around the rest of the stadium. The World Cup at the end of the 20th century has been so expertly rendered corporate that the best seats are exclusively for the suits and, from a short distance away, their uniformly conservative clothing gives them the look of a rich layer of loam soil. The suits in question comprise heads of state, tour- nament officials, sponsors, royalty and football association representatives, none of whom, of course, will be paying their way. Masterton feels a very brief pang of annoyance about this, albeit one anaesthetized by his own pain-free, rapid-transit route to the match. His attention is quickly shifted back to the spectacle of a trapeze artist dressed in the fashion of a medieval jester in a blue, white and red costume suddenly dropping dramatically, as if out of the sky, to dangle only a few feet in front of him, arms pumping, legs flailing and smoke billowing from a blunderbuss-type instrument cradled in his arms.

The acrobats and artistes, after half an hour of colourful cavorting, clear away their props and bustle off the pitch. 'That alone was almost worth the price of the ticket,' Tucks says. 'It was really like an open-air stage production put on by the Comédie-Française.' Masterton nods. 'Molière eat your heart out,' he chuckles, gazing around the spectacular, new, 80,000–seat stadium. 'What would the great man have given for an audience like this?'

There is as yet no action on the field, the players having been compelled to undertake their warm-up on a training pitch underneath the main stand while the day's other performers have been strutting their stuff. To Masterton's right, a dishevelled man in a Glengarry yells at his friend, 'See if they don't come out and wave at us, I'll be really unhappy. I mean, we don't ask for much. We come all this way and the least they can do is come out and give us a wave. Remember that last time? They didn't give us a wave. Spoiled my whole trip that did; so it did . . . that.'

As the three friends continue to await the start of the action, Midge jokes, 'Right, time to get our football headsets on.' Masterton tries to tune in to the occasion; to put on, firmly, his football headset, as Midge suggests. 'Should be an interesting game today,' he tries as an opener then adds, tentatively, for the sake of conversation, 'Did you know that Craig Brown, the manager, spends ninety minutes speaking into a tape recorder when he is observing matches involving opposing teams, and then writes up nine-page reports from his verbal notes?' Tucks and Midge shake their heads in confession of their ignorance. Midge is based in Geneva, where he is working for CERN, the European nuclear research organization, as a high-level technician on the construction of a particle accelerator; Tucks is director of a software company and lives in London – he has taken a day off and travelled over on Eurostar for the match. Neither is fanatical about football but they are enthusiastic about being at the World Cup.

Confident now that he has a receptive audience, Masterton goes on, expansively. 'Yes, apparently Brown has been doing that for years and years. Did you hear what he said about being in this tournament?' Again, his companions shake their heads, expressions blank. 'Well, he said, "We're delighted to be one of the thirty countries, out of one hundred and seventy-two, who managed to qualify." I have to say I think that's impressive, to know exactly how many other countries were involved in trying to get to this World Cup and to remember that two of the thirty-two teams here – the hosts and the holders – did not need to go through the qualification process. It shows we have a manager who really knows his stuff and has a good grasp of detail. So professional . . . I think it suggests a manager who will check everything meticulously, time and time again, and that's what you need to win football matches, don't you think?' His friends nod their heads in quiet agreement.

Encouraged by the lack of challenge to his recently acquired knowledge, Masterton continues, 'Craig Brown also had some interesting things to say about our style of play. You know, he summed it up nicely, I thought, when he said, "Sometimes it looks as though we almost have a fetish about trying to keep possession and that can prevent us making passes at the right time."'

Crawling through Masterton's cranium are some other equally interesting footie facts that he has memorized carefully but his flow of thought is interrupted as the two teams emerge from underneath the VIP area, the Brazilians holding hands in a chain as the Scots stride out, rather less lithely, alongside them. Masterton and his companions, all resplendent in the latest edition of the blue Scotland jersey, really feel part of the event when they see the team in the same gear and applaud with great enthusiasm.

The Tartan Army, in the seventies a ragged, easily inflamed force that, as its name suggested, was always ready for a fight, is now a more easygoing outfit, and chaps such as Masterton, who would have felt badly out of place within its bawdy ranks of a couple of decades ago, find, in the late nineties, that the Scotland football crowd has become as accommodating as a rugby crowd at Edinburgh's Murrayfield: there is a similar feel to the two entities now. Scotland football followers used to become seriously aggressive if they didn't like what they saw on the field – with pitch invasions, casual violence, throwing drinks and scarves at players and managers and hurling bottles among their specialities – but now they see themselves as a spectacle almost on the same footing as the team and with a reputation as fun fans that they are determined to preserve. The modern breed of Scotland fan even seems to thrive on adversity – in the nineties the team has, for the first time, struggled, embarrassingly, against opposition such as San Marino, Estonia and Cyprus – because it adds to their determination to show apprehensive foreigners, wary of the fearsome reputation of British supporters, that the Scotland supporter will remain fanatically friendly even in the face of dire defeat or dreadful draw.

After the match kicks off, Masterton tries to follow the action as best he can, albeit confused by the dizzying, swirling flow of yellow and blue shirts. After only four minutes the Brazilians win their first corner and the ball pings into the roof of the Scottish net at the far end of the field of play without Masterton being sure at all how it got there. 'So much for Brazilian flair,' Masterton says laughingly to his friends, as an antidote to his puzzlement, only to be rewarded for his comment by a look of serious irritation from a fellow Scot in the row in front of them. The giant electronic scoreboard then flashes up the misspelled information, 'Scotland coach – Craig Brow'. Masterton turns to his pals and suggests, 'He of the furrowed—?'

The match weaves onward with barely a sighting of a Scottish player in the Brazil half. The Brazilians are still alternating only between second and third gear but Colin Hendry almost concedes an own goal, heading narrowly past his own post with Jim Leighton beaten and a fierce Roberto Carlos shot is pushed away from goal by Leighton. Soon after, Ronaldo beats three men, cleverly turning Hendry, cruising away from an easily duped Tom Boyd and Darren Jackson and enforcing a fine save from Leighton. The Scots have still not had an effort on target when Kevin Gallacher, shortly before half-time, flops to the ground with César Sampaio at his back, the Brazilian looking like a dopey delivery boy habitually blamed for making a hash of things, and the Spanish referee awards a penalty kick. John Collins strikes it with ice-cool style, beautifully and low into the corner of the Brazilian net.

The Scots keep it at 1–1 for half-time but the match resumes its pattern for the second half, the boys in blue stuttering along, advancing up the field only so far at a time before quickly turning back at the first sign of resistance from the Brazilians, like a miser withdrawing some money from under the bed but immediately, on second thoughts, putting it back. It is a shame because for all that Brazil are a fine attacking force, their defence is not watertight. Cafu and Roberto Carlos, the full-backs, leave lots of space in behind them and Júnior Baiano and César Sampaio, the two centre backs, look very slow and very heavy. The Scots' caution means those defenders remain almost untested and, in sitting deep, the Scottish team plays into the Brazilians' hands, allowing them to exploit their strengths. It suits the South Americans to pick away slowly and steadily at the Scots' defensive puzzle and, in this way, to warm up gently for the rest of the tournament. Dummies and back-heels, almost at training game pace, illuminate the Brazilians' play but it proves to be a pratfall that donates victory to the world champions.

With little more than a quarter of an hour to go, Cafu, the

right-back, once more glides down the wing and eases into the Scottish penalty area, where he stretches out to meet the ball in the air and contorts his lightweight boot with the flexibility of a hand inside a glove to craft a shot at goal. Leighton intercepts and parries only for the ball to bounce off the incoming Tom Boyd and into the Scots' net.

It is a grey, drizzly afternoon as the fans seep away from the stadium. Back into central Paris Masterton and chums go – first to a bar. They are sipping their drinks when a young Frenchman enters, with two girls, and genuine astonishment sweeps across his face to see, early on a Wednesday evening, a number of people milling around in football tops. Then, as if recalling that there is been a minor pop concert or the all-France tiddlywinks championship taking place in the city, he suddenly remembers and tells his female friends, 'Oh yes, I think the World Cup begins here today . . .' Only in France could there be such insouciance about the arrival in town of the greatest tournament on earth, not least one dreamed up by a Frenchman, Jules Rimet, way back when.

Moving on to L'Oiseau Orange, a nearby restaurant, the maître d' takes one look at his latest customers' football shirts and rushes to intercept the waiter who has shown them to their table, just as the latter is about to pluck out three menus for the Scottish guests. Within minutes, three plates arrive and are placed in front of them, each one containing a raw baking potato covered in uncooked herbs. 'Compliments of the house,' the waiter says stiffly just before flouncing away and tossing, over his shoulder, the words, 'I am afraid everything else on the menu is off.' Despite other diners clearly tucking into hearty meals around them, the trio realize there is no point entering a dispute in the face of such Gallic intransigence.

Retiring to another pub, Masterton and friends take a table

to watch Norway play Morocco, to which the bar manager obligingly tunes the television for the benefit of the Scots. Two local types, however, tell their girlfriends to stand up at the end of the bar and block sight of the screen and when the barman sees this and upbraids his regulars an argument breaks out among the French with the locals complaining loudly that this is a bar and not a football stadium. The French, it has to be said, are really going out of their way to make this tournament memorable for their visitors.

· 1998 · 1998 · 1998 · 1998 · 1998 · 1998 · 1998 · 1998 · 1998 · 1998 ·

It's a great game this, this football, in the late 20th century. The pay of the participants has escalated during the past decade to the point where the manager of the national team and the players receive thousands of pounds per week for plying their trade. Surroundings suitable for such cosseted individuals are to be found at the team hotel, the Hostellerie du Vallon de Valrugues in St-Rémy-de-Provence, where, over the following few days, messages and faxes penetrate its five-star walls to tell Boyd that Brazil's second goal wasn't his fault. Such prompt forgiveness seems extraordinary – from an international defender is it too much for the public to expect all-round awareness, anticipation and a bit of acrobatic adjustment to at least try to get out of the way of a ball, or, even better, to expect the occasional nasty rebound, rather than allowing the ball simply to bounce harmfully off his body?

A golf course extends from the *hostellerie* and the players can also relax in a games room or at a superb swimming pool or in Jacuzzis and saunas. The chef will concoct for them

271

anything they might require. There is no sense of feeling trapped or bored in between matches. Tony Blair, the new British prime minister, has been out here to wish the team good luck in the tournament and to chat with them briefly in that clipped, 'I've only got a minute but I'll have a quick chat with you anyway though you must always remember I'm on my way to something more important' matey way of his.

The age of spin is well and truly upon us and the Scots' manager is in great form as he looks back on the match with Brazil and the second group game, against Norway. 'We are becoming one of the best teams in Europe –' Craig Brown tells anyone prepared to listen. The Scotland manager is a softly spoken, balding, tubby fifty-seven year-old, with a grand-fatherly mien and a tremendous line in patter. The Scotland team took fifty-two minutes to get a shot on target from open play against the Brazilians but Brown determinedly goes on '– and I'd certainly say now that we have to underline that [becoming one of the best teams in Europe] by beating the Norwegians, even though they are perhaps the world's form team. Our front two, Kevin Gallacher and Gordon Durie, are very hot at the moment and, given service, they will score.'

Those watching the match in Bordeaux that follows, a 1–1 draw between two robust, northern European teams that are almost scornful of sophistication, might wonder why, as the Scottish team return to while away the hours at their luxurious headquarters prior to their third match, against Morocco, their hopes of remaining in the World Cup hang by the most slender of threads. Even a victory over the North Africans may not be enough to maintain their foothold in the tournament if the result in the Brazil–Norway match, to be played simultaneously, fails to favour Scotland.

If the Scottish supporters are worried they are not showing it. They fill the main square in St-Étienne on the day of the third group match, for their latest festival of self-celebration in an unsuspecting city in a foreign land, quaffing their beer with a desert-like thirst and with the bearing and look of medieval peasants on a feast day. These supporters, while telling everyone how full to the brim they are with pride at being Scottish and how great it is to be so, are still desperately obsessed with 'how ithers see us'. Someone plants a Saltire in the hand of a statue of some bygone French dignitary, possibly someone who quietly dedicated decades of service to their native city, and slightly above his sculpted head, half a dozen kilted individuals, dancing wildly, like garish grotesques, high on a platform above the square, turn around from time to time and proudly lift their skirts to display their backsides in unison. Essential to all this – you might even say its very purpose – is that the locals see, appreciate and enjoy the raw charm and passion of the Scots. Aren't we the finest football fans in the world? Please, please, believe us. Look at us if you don't believe us. Yes, we have taken over your post-industrial town, cleverly re-engineered to make for more conducive modern living with its airy use of light metals and smart street furniture – and we have turned it into something resembling a 14th-century campsite for a doomed army grasping their last hours of pleasure before battle. But you do love us for it, don't you, as we clamber up your traffic lights to shout and sing tunelessly?

Hugh Masterton, Midge and Tucks are part of the 20,000–strong throng cramming the city in advance of today's vital encounter with the Moroccans. As kick-off time approaches, they join the parade of Scots snaking through St-Étienne's ancient alleys and streets toward the Stade Geoffroy Guichard. This trip is another snip for Masterton – only £970 for a return flight to southern France and a night in a four-star hotel. Today he has star-spotted Alex Salmond, the Scottish National Party's main man, wearing a tartan top hat and a not-quite-right, dad's retro Scotland top, posing for pictures outside his downtown hotel.

Masterton recalls seeing the SNP leader anxiously checking a Saltire that was about to be placed in the photograph in case it should feature a politically incorrect slogan and, once satisfied that all was fine, the politician quickly changing his expression from one of concern into a bright, full-frontal smile, face thrust forward for the camera, a fan on either side. Masterton thinks he noticed that Salmond, probably through years of practice, had ensured his face would be just that little bit closer to the lens, more prominent than those of the two Scottish supporters.

Masterton also thinks back to even earlier in the day. He had been outside the train station, having just taken the airport train into town, and was enjoying the warm air. He was wearing designer sunglasses and expensive jeans and a polo shirt – not yet changed into his Scotland shirt for the match – when a Scottish supporter had mistaken him for a local. 'Aw hello there big man,' the diminutive fan had yelled up into his face, 'how's it going an' that. Bonjour an' a' that! Scotland! Eh? Best fitba' fans in the world, eh? We win? Yes?' When Masterton had responded in English and revealed himself not to be a sophisticated, taken-by-surprise local, the one who had accosted him had lost interest and immediately drifted off into the crowd with a backwards look of disgust; almost as if he had been 'had'.

Then there is the question of drink. If you took the prospect of all this senseless drinking away, Masterton ponders, how many would still follow the team, just for the football? The Moroccan supporters dotted around the streets here, for example, are sober and happily chatting over sandwiches or drinking in nothing other than the sights and sounds of a new town and new people. Does this Scotland team stand up to scrutiny through sober spectacles?

· 1998 · 1998 · 1998 · 1998 · 1998 · 1998 · 1998 · 1998 · 1998 · 1998 ·

As they move along toward the stadium, Masterton decides to bring his two expatriate mates up to speed with the football news from home. 'As Craig Brown said after the Brazil game, we gave away two very bad goals from a technical point of view,' Masterton tells them. 'Brown said, "The better team won but we had a great chance not to lose."'

Midge turns and smiles, 'What does he mean by a "technical point of view"? What is that?'

Masterton, slightly confounded by what seems a bit like a challenge to his footballing wisdom, says, 'You'd need to ask him.'

Midge says, 'It sounds like jargon: "technical". It is as if he is hoping subliminally to instil in people's minds that it was almost an accident that Scotland lost – you know, like a technical fault, a mechanical error, something beyond his control. Maybe Mr Brown is a master at using language that will make it seem as if events are beyond his control? Even while, almost paradoxically, remaining the man in charge of the team. Nice work if you can get it.'

'Well, anyway,' Masterton says, 'He also said, we've got to beat Morocco – "no ifs or buts", he said.'

'Well at least that sounds pretty much cut and dried,' Midge responds. 'You can't argue with that. So we might at least see some attacking football tonight.'

Encouraged, Masterton adds, 'Craig Brown says he is "cautiously optimistic" in advance of this Morocco match.'

'"Cautiously optimistic"?' Midge says, again rather too querulously for Masterton's liking. 'What is that one then? Surely you are either optimistic or not? Isn't that a bit like saying, "I'm expecting bright blue skies tomorrow – but I won't be too surprised if it pours down with rain. Or, I'm expecting to win this match but, you never know, the other team might win, too."'

Around them, a mass of bodies in blue shirts perambulates forward slowly. The first verse of *Flower of Scotland* rises from the fans once again, for what seems to Masterton like the 150th time that day. Even in advance of an anticipated match on this cloyingly sultry evening, perfect for watching football, the near-ceaseless repetition of the song has a wearying effect. One man, to Masterton's right, dressed in a Scotland rugby shirt, is being held up by his mates on either side; head nodding toward the ground, eyes shut, he is as lifeless as a Guy Fawkes dummy and has no chance of seeing the match but he is, nevertheless, being transported to the game – almost like a desperately sick person being taken on a religious pilgrimage of which they are aware only on the smallest level.

Masterton throws in one last pearl as the stadium looms up ahead of them. 'Did you know that, at their hotel before they left Glasgow, the team had a talk from a referee to take them through seventeen examples of tackles from behind that could get them sent off at the World Cup? How's that for planning?'

'Well at least they should finish this match with everyone on the field of play,' Tucks says. 'That's something to be "cautiously optimistic" about.'

· 1998 · 1998 · 1998 · 1998 · 1998 · 1998 · 1998 · 1998 · 1998 · 1998 ·

A superficially creditable performance against Brazil; a battle against Norway; what now with the Moroccans? Until relatively recently, such a fixture would equate almost to a promissory note of maximum points for one of the long-established football nations, such as Scotland, but since the late seventies, unheralded countries have had a habit of getting under the skin of larger beasts; and this Morocco team are no makeweights. With several of their players at major clubs in Portugal and Spain, they are a selection of strong, determined, success-hungry boys. Scotland's desperate draw with Iran in the 1978 World Cup and the dispiriting defeat to Costa Rica in 1990 are relatively fresh memories for the Tartan Army but there is still a sense among the supporters that victory and a place in the last sixteen is as good as theirs. 'Now it's down to the luck,' Craig Brown says. For all Brown's affability, there is a chilly cloud of caution that surrounds him: this is a man who, with Scotland seeking an equalizer against Brazil, sent on as substitutes a defensive midfield player and then a left wing-back. Is this a manager who can subvert his seeming instincts and send out a team turbo-charged in search of victory?

The stadium is a mass of Saltires and Lion Rampants and

the stands are tight to the pitch, as they are at British grounds. Scotland begin the match with the energy of a team eagerly tackling a British cup tie. There is much to enjoy in the opening twenty minutes as the Scottish players ping the ball about at an incredibly brisk pace for a World Cup match, albeit without creating any goal-scoring chances. Things then go just a bit flat – the sting is taken out of the game after that early flurry – and just when it is not expected, Morocco are the first side to get a shot on target. Tahar El Khalej flights the ball forward and it bends in the air before dropping over the shoulder of Salaheddine Bassir then sitting up nicely for him to slap a volley into the smidgeon of space between Jim Leighton and his near post to open the scoring.

Two minutes into the second half, Abdeljalil Hadda pursues a ranging pass that curves inside David Weir, in the same manner as Colin Hendry was cut out of the play for the first goal. Hadda, one of several sleek, athletic, attacking players in the Moroccan team, strides away from the defender but manages to flick only a soft shot at goal. Leighton pushes the ball into the air but, horrifically, it glides up high behind the goalkeeper and then drops down slowly over the line with Leighton, arms flapping like a grounded, helpless, big bird, desperately attempting to keep it out of goal. The goalkeeper ends up tangled in the net, like the Moroccans' prize catch, while the opposition celebrate wildly. Half a dozen minutes later, Craig Burley, hair dyed blond for this game to draw extra attention to himself, whacks Bassir from behind and the referee, following the mandate to clamp down on such tackles, makes the unmissable Burley the first Scot to be dismissed in a World Cup finals. With Scotland needing a gee-up to get back in the game, Brown again overlooks the forwards on his bench and throws on Tosh McKinlay, the left-back.

Scotland's efforts become clueless and uninspired; the midfield is flat, and consequently Durie and Gallacher, the strikers, too often look isolated. It is especially disappointing in that Morocco look unsure as to whether to twist or stick on their 2–0 lead and are hugely hesitant now in much of their play. Nothing comes from the Scotland bench to offer a variation on the Scots' too-predictable play. Scotland have become a shambles. With six minutes remaining, Brown throws on Scott Booth, another striker – oh why the hell not, we've got nothing to lose – only to withdraw another, Gordon Durie. Almost immediately, Bassir leaves Tom Boyd floundering with a simple flick over his head and though the Moroccan's shot on goal is rather weak, it receives a deflection, off the thigh of Hendry, that diverts it past Leighton. Bassir and Mustafa El Hadji miss excellent close-range chances in the dying seconds and then it is all over.

Masterton stands in the stadium in a daze after the final whistle sounds. Scotland's collapse in the second half has been so substantial that if someone were to tell him the score had been not 3–0 but double that, he would almost believe it. That, indeed, is the impression he has: of a team swamped. And yet he cannot exit the stadium or even leave his seat for jumping, bouncing Scottish supporters, celebrating furiously in the face of defeat. Hasn't the team just been thumped? He is tempted to check with a fellow fan whether he is missing something – some subtlety that means Scotland have retrieved something from the tournament – but the individual in question, face painted blue and white, features contorted, looks to be beyond communication and Masterton thinks better of it. 'We're bouncy, bouncy, bouncy, bouncy,' chants the man, jumping up and down on his seat in unison with the bulk of the Scottish support. If these fans are happy with what they've seen, maybe he is not such a fish out of water here, not such a naïf, for his lack of footballing knowledge. Drastic, irretrievable defeat celebrated like victory. There is an unreal, fictional feel to it all. You just couldn't make it up.

A FRESH START

The DVD has been running for fifteen minutes when Pim van der Veert asks Gert Bleegers to put it on pause. His assistant obliges and then attends to the lights so that the room is fully illuminated once again when van der Veert turns to address the Scotland squad. They have been watching a montage of stunning clips of the Holland international team, from the 1970s pomp of Johan Cruyff, through Ruud Gullit and Marco van Basten in the 1980s and on to the 21st century and Arjen Robben and Ruud van Nistelrooy. 'Well,' van der Veert says in his Dutch twang, 'one question I now will ask you about what you see. What one thing in what you just viewed you do notice about all the players involved?'

The Scots, uniform in their navy tracksuits, had been

expecting to sit through the type of longer presentation favoured by van der Veert's predecessors, and several look startled at being juddered into life by its early curtailment. One individual, in the back row, is actually asleep; not only asleep but lightly snoring. A hand is raised by a player near the front. 'They are all exceptionally skilled?' he suggests tentatively. 'Fine,' van der Veert responds, 'and true – a fair answer, correct in its way, but not what I look for exactly.' No one else offers a response. Most have been intimidated by the array of skills on display and cannot see farther than that as a link in the film.

'No?' van der Veert says quizzically. 'Okay, then, I give you the solution. It is that they all have one pair of legs, one head and one pair of hands and, of course, everything else in between that you would expect of a person. Just like you. Just like your opponents in this World Cup. Just like every top-level player in the world.

'You all know that you can do such things if you get the chance, don't you? Nothing you have seen – Cruyff turning gracefully as a ballet dancer, Dennis Bergkamp cutting inside to hit the ball into the top corner, Arjen Robben accelerating past defenders as if they are made of stone – is beyond you. These guys don't have the superpowers of some American cartoon action hero from a comic book. They are just like you and I want to see you trying out these things; not shuffling on to the grass field hoping for best, hoping you not to be beaten; before today you've gone on to the field of play bent over like a bunch of witches making spells. I don't want to see that at all. I see that – I quit. I want to see players using the freedom you get when you are playing; using it to best advantage, enjoying it, trying things, expression. So, no training today; instead, spend the rest of your day thinking about that.

'Okay, now I want you all to leave this room soundlessly – and don't wake him up.' He points to the sleeping man.

The players follow van der Veert's directive, leaving the sleeper still snoring. When he finally awakens forty-five minutes later it is because two alarm clocks have erupted – one in each ear – and when he manages to defuse them, he finds the room empty and, at his feet, his suitcase, packed, and a letter from van der Veert thanking him for his efforts with the Scotland squad but also telling him that his presence will not be required at the forthcoming World Cup.

· 2006 · 2006 · 2006 · 2006 · 2006 · 2006 · 2006 · 2006 · 2006 · 2006 ·

The new football ground at Dumbarton has one of the most spectacular backdrops in Britain. From behind its sole stand, rises the spectacular and sheer face of Dumbarton Rock, an ancient stronghold on the River Clyde at one time besieged by Vikings and later a safe refuge for the five-year-old Mary Queen of Scots. Now, in this early summer of 2006, its latest historical role is to provide the background to the final staging post for the Scottish national team prior to their departure for the finals of the World Cup in Germany. The facilities – pristine but basic – of the local, third-division club have been put at the disposal of the team and of van der Veert, a coach appointed to steer the squad through the finals, which they have reached by scraping through a play-off with Slovakia on a squeaky-tight 1–0 aggregate, thanks to a late own goal in Scotland's favour at Hampden Park.

Radical action has been subsequently taken by the SFA, albeit at a very late stage – only two weeks before the fixtures begin in Germany – with the daring appointment of the Dutchman. A radical SFA opted for a fresh start and though van der Veert is a man with a low profile in Britain, he has worked miracles at a number of medium-sized Dutch clubs, elevating them well above their station for extended runs in the UEFA Cup and even, in one notable year, the group stages of that playground of the rich: the Champions League.

Press and public are already keyed up for the World Cup finals but van der Veert betrays no sign of enervation or trepidation at the thought of pitching himself into such an arena for the first time with a team that he will be able to supervise in only one pre-arranged friendly match prior to the tournament getting underway. Now in his mid-fifties, van der Veert is interested by the opportunity of reviving a long-dormant Scotland, whose tremendous teams he can recall from his youth, and whose subsequent decline has puzzled him deeply. He steps off the minibus, a modest mode of transport that, at his behest, has replaced the luxury coach that has previously taken the team from their Loch Lomondside hotel to Dumbarton's quaintly named Strathclyde Homes stadium and as the players emerge to make their way to the dressing rooms, van der Veert tells the elderly kit man and his assistants to step aside and orders half a dozen of the players to haul the kit hampers off the minibus. There is a brief pause during which one or two appear on the verge of criticizing the effrontery of such a demand but they already know enough about van der Veert to be aware that he is no respecter of reputations and, with little further ado, they comply quietly with his request.

Once the players have changed into their training gear, van der Veert asks them simply to begin the training session in the normal way; to do what they have done under previous managers. Two or three of the more experienced men look at each other and then set off around the running track; all two dozen happily jog-trotting in an amorphous pack, some players chatting over their shoulders, a couple chewing gum, all of them happy in a long-familiar, plodding routine.

'Stop, stop, stop,' van der Veert calls out as they complete a lap and return to their starting point. 'What are you? The last time I saw such a display was of the zebras in the animal park. Are you footballers? Do you not like the ball? What is going through your minds when running like this around and around and around, killing off the time like the hands going around and around the clock? It is as if you are on a set of rails, like clockwork toys, not thinking. So, from now, no more running. If you run, you run with a ball; all the fitness you ever need, you can get from being with a ball.'

It is a strange thing to contemplate that a group of professional footballers might puzzle over training with a ball rather than without one; stranger still that such a thing could even be a potential breaking point between them and their new coach but, once again, van der Veert's force of personality wins the day and the international footballers of Scotland, cautiously, awkwardly, uncertainly, venture forth on to the pitch, each with a ball at his feet; each gently shuffling along with it as if it might explode in his face at any moment, so unused are they to being asked to concentrate hard on the sphere that is, after all, at the heart of the game.

'Now,' van der Veert tells them, 'from all of you I want you to make me crazy with delight. You know how this you can do? You will all remain with your ball at your feet, moving around the field, for ten minutes. Okay? I start to time you now.'

The ten minutes over, van der Veert calls the players in to him. Some look mentally exhausted; some just look mental, as always. 'Okay, good,' he says, 'You seemed to get through that even though it looked as though it was maybe something like unfamiliar with you? Yes? Tomorrow, we step it up to fifteen minutes, and so on – until by the time we get to the World Cup finals you can maybe all run with a ball for ninety minutes or something like it? How about that? You can imagine such a thing?'

· 2006 · 2006 · 2006 · 2006 · 2006 · 2006 · 2006 · 2006 · 2006 · 2006 ·

Day two starts with the players being asked to run with the ball at their feet, as promised, once again. They seem more relaxed with the concept today, their running is freer, their confidence in controlling the ball stronger. When the quarter hour is over, van der Veert tells them all to leave the field of play and return their balls to Bleegers. 'That's the last you see of those balls for today.' To van der Veert's satisfaction, there is an obvious degree of disappointment among the players at being deprived of their footballs. He leads them down the tunnel and out into the car park of Dumbarton's stadium, the ancient rock looming up above them. Bleegers puts the bag of footballs away in the minibus and produces another, smaller bag, from which he produces a dozen tennis balls. 'No, Wimbledon it is not for,' van der Veert tells the players. 'We're not looking for you to be champs in that as well.'

He doles out the balls, one to every two men, goalkeepers included, and then sets the pairs of players at intervals along the brick exterior wall of the stadium. 'Okay, you never wondered how Cruyff did it so good? Right, here is where; as a boy from the backstreets of Amsterdam, he starts at the wall of the Olympic Stadium.' The players are told to play the ball off the wall, control it and pass it off the wall to their partner. Again, searching looks of bemusement from the players; again, their growing confidence in van der Veert wins the day and they get on with the exercise.

· 2006 · 2006 · 2006 · 2006 · 2006 · 2006 · 2006 · 2006 · 2006 · 2006 ·

It is a relaxed set of Scots who ease themselves into a third day's training under van der Veert. After twenty minutes of running with football at feet, they go through fifteen with the tennis balls and then it is back on to the pitch, where they each get a full-sized football again and are put through an exercise whereby, one at a time, they have to run from the goal-line to the halfway line with the ball at their feet but without looking at it; instead their eyes must meet those of van der Veert all the way. This creates a chaotic scene with footballs miscontrolled and duly sprayed all over the pitch but the squad are gradually coming around to the manager's methods.

'Master this and you can do lots of good things when you are on the pitch,' van der Veert tells them. 'Look at me and, eventually, you the ball will control automatically – you will feel it better. The ball is your friend and if you do this you can look for your other friends and pass the ball on to them with certainty. If you are looking at the ball, one friend, all the time, how can you know where your other friends are on the field?'

The fourth day sees another new exercise introduced to supplement running with the ball, the tennis ball exercise and keeping the ball under control without looking at it. Van der Veert assembles the players on the pitch and selects two teams: one composed entirely of defenders and the other of attackers. The team of attackers is then instructed that they must defend their goal and cannot cross the halfway line, while the team of defenders is to attack their opponents' goal and remain in the attacking half of the pitch. Grumbles emanate from some players, disgruntled at being asked to abandon their specialist roles. 'What do you mean "that's not your position"?' van der Veert asks them. 'You are footballers – that is all. You should be able to do anything anywhere on the pitch – what do they know of defending who know only defending; or of attacking who know only attacking?

'Think yourself into your new position and it you will help when you come to play. If you are thinking like one attacker here, you will know better what your opponent is doing when it comes to defending in an actual match – and the other way around. You will be refreshed out of your usual routine.' As usual, van der Veert's exhortation, delivered in a Dutch accent, perhaps the most reasonable one in the world, quells all dissent and, as usual, the players enjoy the exercise.

A fifth day sees the players happily go through the routines van der Veert has already established. When the time comes to have the full-scale game of attackers against defenders, he gathers the players around him and points to the far corner of Dumbarton's little ground where a ball boy from the youth squad stands idling with his hands in the pockets of his black tracksuit. Van der Veert tells the players, 'When you score, I want you to celebrate as if that little boy over there is the famous Tartan Army, standing there in that corner, and that this is a big World Cup tie.'

When the goal goes in, after a dozen minutes of play, the entire team piles on top of the scorer, roaring, mouths agape, jabbing fists, for ninety seconds until they find van der Veert standing over them. 'Got it out of your systems?' he asks. 'Right, all of you, I don't want to see celebrations such as that in any of our matches. First, it wastes energy; second, the guy on the bottom can end up with an injury – and I've seen that happen; third, it disrupts concentration for the restart of the match. I lost count of the number of matches I see where a team celebrates a goal like this and then another goal quickly they concedes. What a waste! So from now, we want a gentlemanly handshake and then, as you all get back to your own half, a complete concentration on getting ready for the game to start again. Be professional you all.'

· 2006 · 2006 · 2006 · 2006 · 2006 · 2006 · 2006 · 2006 · 2006 · 2006 ·

Six days in, and after an hour of training at Dumbarton's comely little stadium, Van der Veert calls a sudden halt and tells the players to swap boots for training shoes and file out of the main entrance, following him. He leads them across the car park, past the whisky distillers's offices, then alongside the waste ground that backs on to the football ground, past some grey, glowering tenement housing at the top of Wallace Street and up on to Glasgow Road, one of the town's main thoroughfares. On they proceed, past a newsagent, a launderette and a car repair workshop and then, shortly before the railway bridge that carries trains arriving at and leaving from Dumbarton East, they reach their destination, the Stag's Head, a public house that is just opening for business. Van der Veert, without breaking stride, leads the players, still in shorts and training jerseys, through the entrance and, politely greeting the bemused barman, asks for a coffee for himself and pineapple juice for Bleegers. 'Have what you like,' he says on turning to the squad, gathered rather uncertainly around. 'Relax and drink whatever for you is best for you that you think. So feel free and choose away.'

The players, infused with uncertainty, huddle around, looking at one another, mumbling away, then one of the more senior individuals steps forward, 'Eh, the lads are wondering if you are going to be staying?' he says to Van der Veert.

'Of course I am,' Van der Veert responds. 'Why would I not be? I am with you. You want for me to be all lonely? You know, I could be insulted by that?' Then, addressing the players as a group, he says, 'Boys, boys, feel relaxedly. Please, have what you like.' The players look at one another and several now take the step of approaching the bar, confident they are on solid ground to have a good drink, when Van der Veert adds, 'Can anyone to me give the correct time?'

The players, of course, are without watches, but one of the half dozen die-hard regulars at the bar hunched over their first pints of the day, offers, 'Er, it's ten past eleven'.

'Good, good, thank you, thank you,' van der Veert tells the man, the 'thank' in his Dutch-tinged English sounding like 'tank', and his respondent will duly tell his pals, 'The Scotland manager told me to get tanked – and I took him at his word . . .'.

'So,' van der Veert goes on, looking hard at his watch, 'ten past eleven, yes, and can anyone give me the date? I think the date slot on my watch here wrong must be.'

The barman consults a calendar behind the bar, featuring a picture of a black West Highland terrier alongside a white one and on which the days of the month are marked off one by one. 'Third of June, Mr der Veert,' the barman says.

'Thank you, thank you my friend,' van der Veert says. 'So the date on my watch is not wrong after all – it says the third, too, and that means the start of the World Cup is only six days away. That is . . . How you say? A sobering thought. Is that right thing for me to say in public house? Anyway, sorry, sorry, boys, for me to interrupt you all when you are trying to decide what drink to have at this time.'

Soon, trays laden with orange juice, Coca-Cola, apple juice, coffee and tea are making their way to the tables where the players find they can, after all, relax fully in each other's company without the lubrication of alcohol.

· 2006 · 2006 · 2006 · 2006 · 2006 · 2006 · 2006 · 2006 · 2006 · 2006 ·

'I don't like to give anyone much time anyway,' van der Veert says. 'Not me nor to the players. My aim everywhere I have been is quickly to get out of the players a little bit more than they think they can bring. That was true of all my clubs in

Holland and with Scotland I was, how you say, flabbergasted at how much the players had been – I am searching for the right word. Maybe it is repressed? Is that right? Repressed? They had ability but it was as if it did not fit with being a Scottish professional player, even at international level, that you should show that ability, free it up, express it. I don't know why things were like that when I took over but that is how was it; how I found it to be anyway.

'My job was to look at things from a new position. I think sometimes in Scotland the idea had been that coaching players is about making them do exactly what the manager or the coach told them; as if they the players were, yeah, something not to be trusted, like robots without minds of their own. It is not like that – the job of the coach is to extract the talent from the players and get them to think about how to use it for themselves and for the team. When the players discovered just how much they could do, yeah, it was giving excitement not only in me but in the group of players. So we had fourteen days before the World Cup and in every one of those days I plant a new thought in their heads, then I watched the idea bud and then I saw it grow like a flower – until the whole project was blooming well . . .'

'Blooming well what?' asks his Scottish television interviewer as van der Veert trails off.

'Blooming well – only,' van der Veert says.

'Blooming well only what?'

'Blooming well only. Only – blooming well.'

Darkened television studios are the same all over the world, van der Veert muses as he looks around him. Always the same, with the section to be seen on screen brightly lit, shiny, attractive, while behind the cameras scruffy technicians and other operatives gloomily attend, almost listlessly, to their various functions in the murky half-light; or maybe the lit-up section just seems to drain all the energy away from the rest of the place. Van der Veert has been hurried here to this studio in Hanover to explain the 'Scottish miracle' – how an unheralded team has managed to start the World Cup with a 6–0 victory over Ukraine, followed by a draw with Tunisia in their subsequent group match and then a win over Saudi Arabia to clinch top spot in their group. A 3–1 victory over Spain has now taken the Scots into a quarter-final with Brazil. It is spectacular progress for a team that flopped so painfully badly in France in '98 and that failed to qualify for the tournaments either side of that disaster, in 1994 and 2002.

'The players are very committed,' van der Veert goes on, 'but sometimes you can do a little bit more to get extra efficiency out of a player. I think everybody can expect a lot from this Scotland team in energy and passion but my job is to bring a little bit more, you know? Going far in a World Cup is, I think, every time, new; you are in the last eight of the world and it's tight, very tight. We have done well but we can improve by playing bit by bit better. We are practising a lot to achieve that. To do that we leave our egos at the door.'

· 2006 · 2006 · 2006 · 2006 · 2006 · 2006 · 2006 · 2006 · 2006 · 2006 ·

The Scots' training sessions are almost as demanding as the matches in which they participate; sometimes even more so. The results have been revelatory to those who had expected the Scots to be mere makeweights at this World Cup, as in

1998, when they finished 27th out of 32, but van der Veert plays down any idea that this can be described as a miracle. 'No,' he says firmly. 'A miracle is a baby surviving a plane crash or something like that. No, this was a case of combining organization with imagination. Would you expect me to win the World Cup with a disorganized Scotland?

'As far as I can see, before I arrived, football has been both important to Scotland and not important enough. What I mean to say is that a lot of people in Scotland loved football, loved the national team but there was no real depth of thought about it all; it was almost a case of, "Just let us go on the pitch." Then after that the coaches came along and said, "Right, let's get organized," but they got grey-office-organized; stifling the players, no breathing space – no air conditioning. Your country has always possessed very talented players but in the recent times, they could not cultivate their own image, their personality in terms of showing the people what they could offer, what they could give. They can now. Allowing them to show their skills without fear has been a bit like giving a hungry man a hot meal. And why field so many old players in the past, like at France in '98? That can never work.'

There is indeed a notably sharp appetite evident in the Scots as they tackle the Brazilians. Sure, Brazil are world champions but that in itself brings them problems, with players who won that title four years previously still soldered on to the team even if the visual evidence suggests they may be living off the fat of their reputations. While Ronaldinho is fading, Ronaldo has bulked out; not his reputation but his girth. Dida is the latest in a long line of Brazilian goalkeepers who potter around their goalmouth, occasionally dropping things with a clang like an absent-minded Sunday afternoon gardener in his potting shed. Cafu and Roberto Carlos have lost much of the zip that made them the world's most potent attacking full-back pairing a decade ago.

So when, after fifty-seven minutes, Darren Fletcher sends a forty-yard chipped pass scooting through the Brazilians' defence, James McFadden can cut inside Roberto Carlos and, with the instep of his left boot, bend the ball around a flat-footed Dida. 'Calm down and carry on as if it were 0–0,' van der Veert tells Christian Dailly, the Scotland captain, from the touchline as the players trot back coolly low-key in preparation for the resumption. The message spreads throughout the team: they remain in control and click back into the vibrant, high-tempo game that has brought them the lead. The Brazilians find that the Scots, unlike so many teams, do not take a step back, mentally or physically, through being in the lead and the sole goal is all that is needed to send Scotland into the semi-finals.

'Brazil, sadly, is no longer swinging and flaming,' van der Veert says, unapologetically, after the match. 'I see defenders use their boot to make fly the ball into the stands. Have they without shame in themselves? Scotland must never play like that; not for as long as if I am coach. If we did, people would be right to murder me. Our style has the world taken by surprise and that in me gives great pride. I cannot come to a World Cup and try to win in an ugly way – that is like getting invite to beautiful home with beautiful host and then bringing out the bad table manners for everyone to watch. Instead, I have convinced my players they are the best in the world and they have accepted it. That made the barriers fell away.'

This Scotland team does not challenge referees or their assistants; 'a big, big waste of energy' according to van der Veert. It does not take short corners; 'a waste of resources' according to van der Veert. Corners are slung into an area only slightly in advance of the penalty spot, thereby just about eliminating the goalkeeper, and players are not allowed to linger inside the six-yard box when awaiting a corner coming over. 'How can you spring up and jump if there is no space to run at the ball?' the manager has asked his players in training at Dumbarton when they first ran through corners. Instead players line up on the edge of the penalty area, immediately placing their opponents on the back foot when the ball comes whirling into the box.

At the conclusion of a match, the Scottish players are strictly forbidden from seeking out illustrious opponents with whom to swap shirts; van der Veert's theory is that not only is this a potential distraction but that it builds subconsciously into players a sense of inferiority. Instead, the Scotland players are instructed to shake hands calmly with their opponents and then head for the tunnel; if an opponent should request to swap a shirt, then fine. When a scoring opportunity is missed, players in the vicinity of the 'culprit' are forbidden from doing that glaring and gesticulating thing at them as if to say, 'I was in more space, you should have passed to me. I would have scored'. That type of spoiled, selfish egotism is not encouraged.

Through these and stacks of other small matters, Scotland have arrived at, and progressed through, this World Cup relaxed, refreshed and re-energized.

'Football comes down to tiny details,' van der Veert says, 'and words and good ideas can have an extremely stabilizing effect. The boys were enjoying ourselves out there today and we were playing incredible football. We could have gone on for another two or three hours. Good or bad luck doesn't exist in football. All that matters is doing things properly.'

It is to be France in the semi-finals; another team that seems to be coasting on its reputation; the World Cup winners of 1998 only just squeaked through their group but, still, players such as Thierry Henry and Patrick Vieira strut around as if the World Cup trophy will come to them magnetically. They give the impression that undergoing each ninety minutes along the way is just so much mucky business they must put up with if they are once again to get their hands on the golden trophy. Scotland are different. 'They listen to Gert and me with big, big ears,' van der Veert says of his young team. 'And our boys are at the table; hungry for the victory, they have the fork at the ready in their hands. I reject the idea that however it goes it will have been a great occasion for us just being here. We'll see who has the greater hunger.'

McFadden, one of those players who disport themselves best at international level, where the game is less frenetic and more technical than at club level, is quick to test the French, a side that, with an average age of thirty-one, is one of the oldest ever fielded in a World Cup finals. He glides in from the right and adjusts his body for a left-footed shot that Fabien Barthez pushes away from inside his right-hand post. 'What he can do with his feet, some people can't even do with their hands,' van der Veert says of McFadden. 'Sometimes when he plays it seems like he is dancing with the ball. When the ball goes to his feet, it smiles.' Next, Darren Fletcher's twenty-five yard shot goes goalward but swoops down just too late and dips behind the goal, with Barthez stumbling around anxiously.

The French, having survived the Scots' early and energetic flurry, begin to move the ball around impressively. There is not long to go before half-time when Thierry Henry, who has so far moved around like a man on medication, takes the ball inside Gary Caldwell and as the Frenchman moves past him, the Scotland centre-back catches the forward's left shin with his boot. Henry corkscrews to the turf and the Uruguayan referee signals for a penalty kick. Zinedine Zidane strikes the ball beautifully and it whistles directly towards the left-hand corner of the net. Craig Gordon gets a hand to it but the ball still streaks into goal, putting the French 1–0 ahead at half-time.

Henry quickly seeks to add to the one-goal lead shortly after the interval, dashing almost to the goal-line before slashing in a low, hard ball that looks to be going across the face of goal until Gordon attempts to save and diverts it ninety degrees off course but also, fortunately for the goalkeeper, the wrong side of the post and behind for a corner-kick. France – silky, assured – now draw deep on their experience at this level and that compensates for them no longer having the running in their legs that they once did. They don't create much but they keep the ball shuttling around at speed and it is only thanks to the eccentric Barthez that the Scots finally, late in the game, obtain the opportunity to equalize. When McFadden's twenty-yard free-kick comes zooming in at him, Barthez opts to palm the ball crazily up in the air, where it hangs perfectly for a Scottish head to make the connection. Dailly rises to meet the ball but the chance is so good that Lee Miller does the same, simultaneously, and though the striker quickly realizes he will do best to get out of the way, Dailly's header, as a result of this momentary distraction, flies inches over the bar and plops down on the roof of the net. Another late opportunity falls to McFadden but Barthez is quick to spring off his line and McFadden's shot travels over the crossbar. It is France and not Scotland who travel onward.

'Why didn't we win?' van der Veert asks the press, but rhetorically, before they can even get one question in. 'Because we let in a goal. In football, not just in football, but in sport, you win and you lose. How many times have we won? And no one asked why, or only a few people asked, why we won. But you win and you lose. We lost. We still think we should have gone further because it's not always the best players that win but sometimes the best team, and we felt we had the best team. We brought twenty-two players together and made them the best team possible. Nobody was more important than the team. A player cannot make the team but the team can make a player. For me, that's the truth.

'We started a few weeks ago with this project of going into the final stage of the World Cup and we nearly got there. They are fantastic guys. We asked them to change their computer chips and they did. The house was in order when I came – we just needed to buy some new furniture.

'As for arriving here and taking on some big teams, with big reputations, well, the monster only looks frightening when it is in the distance. When you look it in the eye, you often find you were wrong to be afraid. That is the story of this World Cup and of this Scotland. It shows how much you can achieve when you really believe and don't buy into some inferiority of feeling. Before, and for a lot of years with Scotland, it was about being good enough not to lose – now it is all about being good enough to win.

'We worked from the first day. We didn't give excuses to get used to each other – my way of working or their way of playing – and they reacted in a second. From the first it was very positive. If Scotland are to go forward from here, then this is the way it must continue.'

LAST CALL

Even now, it seems like the most pleasant and relaxing sort of a dream; one of those from which the sleeper awakes refreshed and happy and re-energized. The dreamlike experience is that of Scotland finding themselves present at the 2010 World Cup in South Africa. So late has been their gilt-edged invitation to this year's competition that they have found themselves almost unable to make it at all and when they do it still feels as though they are in the midst of some particularly enjoyable reverie.

Four days before the tournament is due to start, this June of 2010, the tremors that lead to Scotland's World Cup hopes being resurrected begin when an earthquake is detected by Japanese seismologists and within hours North Korea has proudly proclaimed that in honour of their leader, Kim Jong-il, they have carried out a nuclear test. A swiftly released official government communiqué embroiders the hard facts in the uncompromising language of the isolated state:

> South Koreans, by day or night, can no longer sleep easy in their beds: for retribution is on the horizon. You may not see the horizon that holds your fate and you may not see the weapon levelled against you but that does not mean it is not there. Nor should the citizenry of the United States of America feel a sense of complacency at this time. As the proverb says, 'You may not even be aware that the monkey on your back has landed before it begins scratching.'

It is a statement that clashes somewhat with FIFA's avowal to bring the world together through football, given that both North Korea and South Korea are preparing for the finals in South Africa at the latest gathering of what Sepp Blatter, the president of FIFA, calls the 'FIFA football family'. Japan and the USA are other family members to be discomfited by this threat from the FIFA family's black sheep. 'Monkeys should remember that when they start to fly fast through the trees,' a US government statement responds, 'unseen obstacles may hit them especially hard and fast.' North Korea's reply is to the point: 'As the proverb says, "He who wants banana from tree must look over his shoulder for monkey will not be far away."' The US responds: 'Monkey should watch for the gorilla hiding behind the tree.' North Korea replies, 'Ooh, ooh, ooh, ooh, ooh, ooh, ooh – Monkey fast, monkey got pace – America watch monkey don't whack its face.'

Within twenty-four hours of North Korea's declaration, and with the finals only seventy-two hours away, eleven of the thirty-two members of the football family who are readying themselves for the finals, spearheaded by the Japanese, the Americans and the South Koreans, tell FIFA firmly that they will be returning home in protest unless North Korea are ejected from the tournament. FIFA, behind the scenes, negotiate frantically with the North Korean FA, suggesting a retraction of their government's bellicose statements, which have been pouring forth hourly from the capital, Pyongyang, in the wake of the nuclear test, but they refuse, unequivocally, even to contemplate such a thing.

It is early on the Thursday morning of 10 June that FIFA announce, 'It is with the greatest regret that we have decided we have no choice but to invite the Democratic People's Republic of Korea kindly to withdraw from this year's World Cup. We take this course of action only as a last resort and with a heavy heart but due to circumstances with which the entire world is familiar, we feel we have no option but to do so for the sake of the harmony of the game and the well-being of the world's football family as a whole.'

The FIFA spokesman omits to add that a behind-the-scenes trade-off has seen the North Koreans promised the hosting of the next World Cup to be held in Asia, in 2022, in return for leaving the 2010 stage without any further fuss. The immediate concern of world football's governing body is not a dozen years hence but that their great football fest is now just twenty-four hours away and, with thirty-one teams, it is looking lopsided – and FIFA does not like its image clouded by anything messy. Another nation has to be invited at short notice, but which one?

One of the North Koreans' many demands for shuffling away silently is that they are not to be replaced with another country from their region, so FIFA apparatchiks frantically scan the rest of the world's qualifying groups in search of the nation which has failed to reach the finals but that has the best case for inclusion as North Korea's replacement. It is a futile chase: whenever one nation suggests itself, another pops up with just as good a case. The hours are ticking away when, late on the Thursday afternoon, Fritzy Smauth, the official behind many of FIFA's PR initiatives, is presented with the solution. 'Hey,' he tells the world's media at a hastily convened press conference inside the Cape Town International Convention Centre, 'good to see you guys. And for you good guys we good people have got some good, good news.'

Despite the sense of emergency bordering on crisis that has been enveloping FIFA people during the past two days, Smauth looks as though he has just emerged from a fort-night's break at a secluded Swiss spa. 'Stress is just a four-letter word with fifty per cent extra,' is one of his favourite sayings, 'and I never acknowledge four-letter words; they are rude and unnecessary.' As with most of Smauth's well-prepared aphorisms, by the time the listener has worked it out, the peerless PR man has moved on to the next one. It's true that he never swears, never gets flustered and even now, here, under hot television spotlights, and in front of the furrowed brows on the crumpled faces of the habitually scruffy media set, he wears a ready, knowing, smile on his near unlined, buffed shiny, middle-aged face. A sleek, pinstriped suit, with powder-blue shirt and gold tie setting it off spec-tacularly, rose handkerchief sprouting from the top pocket of the jacket, completes the picture of unhurried assurance. In his right hand he holds his gold, half-moon glasses and in his left the soon-to-be-distributed press release in which his announcement is noted. Just before beginning his official state-ment to the media, he scrutinizes the release, briefly, with a half-smile on his face, as if making sure he is not about to miss out anything important, but there is really only one thing everyone needs to know: the name of the country that will replace North Korea.

'Ladies and gentlemen,' he says eventually, languidly putting down the sheet of paper on the lectern – he stands alongside rather than behind the lectern, to provide an informal impression, 'thank you so much for assembling here at such short notice. One or two of you may be aware that we are short in numbers for this World Cup . . . if you'll forgive me my little joke . . . Anyway, FIFA has carefully considered all of the implications of this and has decided that the FIFA family must have a full complement of members for the tournament to be the huge success that it always is. We searched around the world, looked at the record of everyone in the qualifying competitions, and discovered that there were so many teams who had done so well that it was impossible, and unfair, to separate the best of them. We at FIFA place above everything else,' a quick flourish of the hands, 'the harmony of the FIFA football family and, so, we wanted to go into this World Cup with no question of any dispute hanging over our heads. With this in mind, we have not, therefore, chosen any of the teams placed second in the qualifying groups.'

Though aware that his words have stirred the interest of the assembled media, who now, in the absence of a second-best, wonder which team on earth can possibly have been chosen to fill the void, Smauth takes his time before continuing. 'So, having considered everything, all the attendant circumstances,' he goes on, rubbing his hands together unctuously and smiling simultaneously, as he takes a step forward, 'we, FIFA, have decided that the vacant position should go to a nation that has graced the competition so wonderfully well over the years and, with respect to the others whom we will miss so much this summer, there is only one nation that fits perfectly – and that nation is Scotland.'

· 2010 · 2010 · 2010 · 2010 · 2010 · 2010 · 2010 · 2010 · 2010 · 2010 ·

It was only minutes before Smauth's conference began that the Scottish Football Association had been informed that the vacated place was being awarded to their nation – it is important to FIFA that it is they who break the news rather than the Scots themselves, even if this shaves several hours off the already absurdly brief time that the Scots have to bring together a team and get themselves out to South Africa.

The inclusion of Scotland as replacements for North Korea is, in fact, a piece of FIFA mendacity dressed up as goodwill. Scotland are a pale shadow, now, of their illustrious predecessors of the 1960s, 1970s and 1980s and fit FIFA's practical requirements perfectly in that the three other countries drawn alongside North Korea will be very unlikely to protest that the Koreans have been replaced by tougher opponents. With Scotland not expected to go too far, it is also anticipated that the major nations in the tournament will also not be able later on to complain that they have been unsettled by the installation of a sleek, fast-moving, dark horse.

It has been a tough few years for followers of the Scottish team. Their qualifying campaign for the 2010 finals unravelled spectacularly as a selection of players stumbled, amid a degree of drunkenness and hit-and-miss team management, to finish third behind Holland and Norway in their group, with South Africa and the finals seemingly little more than a cruel mirage to the team's followers. Not that the principal players were feeling the pain for too long. This early June, most of the players who fumbled their way through the qualifying campaign are taking a holiday, and have scattered to disport themselves upon various of the best beaches the world can offer; few are bothering to keep in touch regularly with home and how everyone else is tuning up for the tournament. Consequently, despite frantic global calls to mobile telephone numbers by SFA officials this Thursday evening, in the few hours the Scots have to assemble a squad, a number of players who have made frequent appearances over the past couple of years are discovered to be unreachable – thoroughly off-message: some have simply switched off their mobiles, others have bought new mobiles with new numbers, to make them beyond communication while on holiday. SFA officials, funnily enough, have not been among the select few whom they have decided they would like to hear during their annual break.

The Seychelles and the Maldives and the Cayman Islands, respectively, are playing host to three of the players who have been first-choice Scotland regulars recently and not one of the three is on call. In the Mexican resort of Cancun, half a dozen others, having completed their holidays with families and partners, have met up to re-enact the drinking session at Loch Lomond that scarred the Scots' campaign in early 2009 and, thus, this Thursday evening they are entirely beyond the reach of anyone or anything. A couple of others are, at the moment when the SFA attempt to contact them, in places where they shouldn't be at all and so have put themselves deliberately out of contact. With the Scots scrabbling frantically around to find players ready to fly out to South Africa on the following day, in time for their first scheduled game, on the Monday, it means that a number of younger, hungrier players, unable to

afford to indulge in long, lingering holidays in far-flung desti-
nations for the entire close-season and already back at home
are thrust forward for selection. Their inclusion in the squad
– which should, anyway, have been hastened given the poor
quality of their seniors' performances – is now fast-tracked.

With, at this late stage, almost every flight from Europe
to South Africa fully booked to carry the majority of the visiting
500,000 supporters to the tournament, the Scots find that the
only tickets available to them include a ten-day, upmarket
safari with accommodation on a game reserve and at a cost
of £16,000 per head. Soon after the players' arrival, they accompany the safari-holiday guests on a jeep tour to view the
wildlife. The squad has been split into two batches of eleven
for the two jeeps allotted to them by the tour company; one
eleven is the starting line-up for Scotland's opening match,
the other the reserves.

'I don't think they'll have any of your sort out here,'
Christophe Berra, the Wolves centre-back, yells to Leigh
Griffiths, the Dundee striker, above the roar of their jeep as
it veers off across the dry, dusty veldt. 'Hey, remember when
he had his hair like a badger – big white streak in the middle,
black on the sides? What was that all about wee man? Anyway,
I think it'll be bigger stuff than badgers we'll be seeing out
here.' Griffiths racks his brain to respond to Berra. 'Well, Mr
Wolf, what time is it, eh?' he laughs. 'Will we be seeing any
wolves out here? Other than you, eh, will we?'

Berra laughs. 'That the best you can do wee man?' he says.
Then he turns to Craig Gordon. 'But we will be seeing some
giraffes, apart from you and big Kev, won't we?'

Gordon grins along with Kevin McDonald, the young
Burnley player. 'We will – and some laughing hyenas maybe,
like yourself and this guy here,' Gordon replies. He motions

toward Alan Hutton, recipient of this description, who, in turn, addresses Lee Wallace. 'Remember, you're not allowed to shoot at the animals with that airgun of yours, wherever you're hiding it.'

Like most of the humour between footballers, you really have to be there to enjoy it to the full – and so it goes on, with James McFadden, Darren Fletcher, Graham Dorrans and Darren Barr, other first-team choices, all patiently awaiting their turn to be the butt of the banter, every player on a similar level of contentment at simply being here so unexpectedly, with no time for boredom, recriminations or fatigue to set in.

· 2010 · 2010 · 2010 · 2010 · 2010 · 2010 · 2010 · 2010 · 2010 · 2010 ·

There is a danger, when facing Brazil, of playing the name and not the team. Their sunburst-yellow shirts can have a dazzling effect on opponents, as can the litany of globally familiar names that every Brazilian World Cup team contains. It is something that might be expected to have an effect on this youthful Scottish team as they stride out at Ellis Park, Johannesburg, for both teams' opening fixture in the 2010 World Cup.

Such doubts can be safely set aside when Darren Fletcher, with leonine tenacity, hunts down and wins the ball from a dilatory Robinho within seconds of the kick-off and threads a pass to James McFadden, who dodges past two hefty Brazilian attempts at tackles before being hacked down twenty yards from goal. McFadden, Fletcher and Leigh Griffiths hover over the free-kick, to be taken from slightly to the right of the 'D'. It is Griffiths who runs at the ball, judging his attempt on goal so well that it ruffles the hair of the Brazilian on the far end of their defensive wall and by the time Júlio César, in the Brazilian goal, realizes the ball is on its way to the top left-hand corner, the only thing he can do is admire the precision with which the ball fits into the space just below the crossbar and just inside the post to send into the lead a Scotland team that, like so many of their predecessors, are hugely determined to make their mark on this world – and its cup.